The Mountains of Iron

A history of the Iron Mining industry in mid-Antrim

By Kevin J. O'Hagan

Above: Glenravel Mine, Tunnel Level
Opposite page from top: Crusher building known locally as the Wash house;
Crommelin's Furnace; Water tower and Stationmaster's house, Parkmore

CONTENTS

Published in 2016 by Shanway Press, 15 Crumlin Road, Belfast BT14 6AA

Cover design: David-Lee Badger

ISBN: 978-1-910044-12-4

INTRODUCTION

To have even a passing interest in disused mine workings may seem to many people an odd, even crazy, pastime but to me it has been an obsession for a long number of years. It arose initially through the sport of caving, mainly because the caving areas of Ireland are fairly widely scattered and the nearest is nearly 100 miles away. The reasons for delving into the bowels of the Earth are as numerous as those for climbing mountains and can only be appreciated by those who have been where no man has been before and have seen another world. Mines are different in this respect but the excitement of any exploration is hard to resist and at any rate there were other factors which drove me. My father and grandfather had been iron-ore miners and I was born in the heart of the mining district, in fact, within a stones throw of the birthplace of the mining industry, yet I knew nothing of the history of the mines and no one knew the whole story.

I resolved, therefore, to find out for myself and so began many years of exploration and research into these mines. A motorist driving through the area or a bus passenger, who would have more time to look around, could not fail to notice the red spoil heaps like miniature volcanoes dotted among the fields and hill slopes beside the main road from Martinstown to Parkmore. Nor could he miss the old railway embankments, cuttings and sidings running off to the mine workings from the main line which ran roughly parallel to the main road. These too were my first knowledge of the existence of the mines when as a schoolboy I travelled this road and had time to look but not to understand. A long time was to elapse before my curiosity turned to active interest. Such interest to be effective and worthwhile must cover such topics as mining technology, geology, industrial archaeology and to a large degree local history.

Armed only with the knowledge that mining had taken place at some time in the past the next task was to confirm and enlarge upon it by research into old maps, books, manuscripts, letters and local knowledge. From these I learned the extent of the mining industry in the Glenravel area and beyond and in particular the locations of the main mines.

It was quickly realised that to cover such an extensive area was not a job for one person. Furthermore as I intended to explore any mines which were still open it was imperative that I should have company since underground exploration is extremely hazardous for the individual. I enlisted the help of some friends who quickly developed an interest in the subject and were keen to go underground.

Our first task was to investigate every mine level, air shaft and abandoned working in the area. This involved a lot of practical fieldwork, tramping round the hills in all sorts of weather but all good healthy exercise. The Ordnance Survey maps of the area (6in scale) proved extremely useful in this respect and each mine level was systematically checked and its condition noted. These maps, last revised in 1921 and now out of print, show in great detail every feature – houses, streams, fences, mines, air shafts, mineral railways etc. The names of the mines shown read like a Who's Who of the mining industry – Herd's Drift, Walker's Drift, Salmon's Drift (a derivative of Solomon's Drift) and Crommelin Mine. Most of the others were known by the townland in which they were situated – Tuftarney Mines (Ironstone), Tuftarney Mines (Bauxite), Ballynahavla Mine, Glenravel Mine, Parkmore, Evishacrow, Cargan and Dungonnell Mines. The Mountcashel Mines were named after the company which worked them but were known locally as the Bleagh Mines. They included the whole group of mines on the north western slope of Carncormick.

In all over 100 levels and shafts were examined over a lengthy period, representing about 45 different mines and illustrating clearly the extent of the mining industry in this part of Mid-Antrim.

From this it will be realised that the area between Martinstown and Parkmore must have been a real hive of industry around the turn of the century. The narrow gauge trains themselves must have been fascinating to watch as they carried ore out of numerous sidings to the main line and later conveyed passengers from Parkmore to Ballymena and back. From the main line these sidings went off to the various groups of mines with stations for loading and unloading and goods and engine sheds. A novel feature associated with the mineral railway was the windlass situated on top of a hill just north of Cargan village. This became known locally as 'the Drum' and its purpose was to help empty ore wagons up the Drum Brae, a steep incline or gravitational incline plane with 1 in 11 gradient, which could not have been negotiated without this mechanical device. The remains of the Drum can still be seen today, just two bare walls perched like a sentinel on the skyline, a relic of a once thriving industry, now a skeleton of the changing times. At Ardclinis on the coast a faint outline remains of the track of an incline on the steep mountainside. Both drums used the principle that laden ore wagons going down helped pull the empty ones up.

After all the mine levels etc had been looked at a list was made denoting their condition. Some of the open mines had accumulated substantial quantities of water over the years since mining ceased and this was a deterrent at first. Some of those which were blocked had possibilities of being reopened with a little digging but no attempt was made to do this at this early stage. It remained therefore to investigate only those mines which had dry entrances.

We started with the Glenravel Mine in the townland of Legagrane, one of the numerous mines on the south side of Slievenanee. This was a suitable beginning to our explorations since it was here that underground mining began back in 1867. It proved to be a very dry mine apart from one passage with ankle-deep water. Its workings ranged from flat out crawls to one passage over five metres high and was so extensive that even after numerous visits to it we have still not been through all of it. It is one of the safest mines in the area with only minor evidence of roof collapse but not suitable for the inexperienced or field tripper due to the extremely low areas which have to be negotiated to reach the higher workings of the interior.

Once a start had been made we continued to explore the other mines, often going back several times to check other passages, take photographs and measurements. We took to the water and explored the wet mines, notably Parkmore Mine which we had to swim into and Herd's Drift which had chest-deep water most of the way. We also descended a 60-foot air shaft to the Parkmore Mine only to find it blocked by various types of rubbish. Such disappointment, however, is commonplace in underground exploration and did not deter us. One mine which we intended to dig out was the Crommelin Mine. The adit had been built up by the miners about 10 feet in and would have been a simple matter to gain access. For this reason we left it for some time thinking it would remain as we first found it. Alas, when we returned in late 1975 no trace of it could be found. The whole area round the mine had been levelled by bulldozer and the entrance and a nearby air drift had been obliterated.

Perhaps this is inevitable in our changing world and in years to come no doubt other mines will be lost to progress, greed or bureaucracy. This has already happened with the air shafts, Herd's Drift and Cargan Mines. Fortunately, the Crommelin Mine is only a small part of a very extensive complex which was accessible by other routes and which has been explored on countless occasions with the aid of the original plans and has been used for many field trips and TV footage.

Mining in Northern Ireland today is virtually non-existent, at least in the underground sense, but a vast reawakening of interest in mining and mineral resources is taking place throughout the country, the latest of these being the mining of lignite around the shore of Lough Neagh and at Ballymoney and of gold in the Sperrins. New minerals will no doubt be found and old minerals may become profitable enough to be reworked and perhaps this province will again see the bustle of mining activity which was taking place here over a hundred years ago.

At that time mines were operating across the country – coal at Ballycastle and Coalisland, rock salt at Carrickfergus, lead at Conlig and iron-ore and bauxite at several locations but mostly at Glenravel where one of the most extensive ore fields in the country was in full production.

This book is not intended as a guide to the mines of Glenravel and district since it is unlikely that anybody will ever want or be able to visit them, especially now that all the open adits have been closed or gated. Those mines that were formerly accessible are, in general, quite safe due to a sound basalt roof although dripping water, deep pools and some very low workings are common. No one should venture underground without adequate and proper lights and never alone – it would be quite easy to become a statistic.

It is not my intention to explain in detail the complexities of the formation of iron ore and bauxite or the differences between the bauxites of one area and those of another since these matters have been fully documented elsewhere and by those more qualified than I to write about them. Instead, I will attempt to explain in simple terms the series of events which led to the formation of the massive beds of the Antrim lavas and in the process produced the rich mineral seams which gave rise to the mining industry. In the area under consideration two main phases of mining activity can be identified – the period from the mid-19th century to the early decades of the 20th and the period of the Second World War. I do not propose to dwell long on the second period of mining which was undertaken for the war effort. This is mainly for two reasons.

The earlier period of mining is the more interesting from the point of view that there is more history attached to it and during its beginnings none of us were around. To know what our forefathers, grandparents or parents did, how they lived and worked etc. is infinitely more exciting than what we ourselves did or can remember. The mining years 1939 to 1945, on the other hand, are still not too far distant which brings me to my second point.

The five or six years of the war cover such a short period compared to the earlier phase of sixty to seventy years from 1866, and played such a small, albeit important, part in the story of the Co. Antrim mining industry. If there had been no war it is unlikely that the mines would have been worked since they were opened purely to provide a source of aluminium for the manufacture of war planes. With the ending of the war there was no further demand for aluminium and the closure of the mines soon followed.

For those who are only interested in the Glenravel Mines from an historical point of view this book should fill a gap and hopefully bring back memories of friends and ancestors who toiled beneath the hills a hundred and more years ago.

To those not old enough to remember or even to know it should be an eye-opener into what went on in this district when the iron ore industry was at its peak, the reasons for its decline and the explanation of the evidence that remains.

It is hoped too that the information contained in this book will be a useful contribution to the historic literature of the Glens since it was through the provision of better rail, road and harbour facilities for the mining industry and the enterprise of the mining companies that the most famous of the Nine Glens became easily accessible to the general public of the period and to the tourists of today.

Finally, I should add that with the continued expansion of our towns and villages through the development of land for new factories and housing estates we inevitably have to yield sites of archaeological and historical interest to the bulldozer. It is hoped that this book will help to record and preserve in some form those sites which, through various housing and farm improvement schemes, will be altered or erased from the landscape, so removing an integral part of our history. To a certain extent much has already been lost through afforestation at Parkmore and Glenariff. In years to come much more will disappear, old mine and railway buildings will crumble, the mineral railways will become obliterated or unrecognisable and mine entrances will be filled in, become overgrown or collapse. It will only be through the records that are kept that this episode of our industrial and historical heritage will be remembered and a link with the past maintained.

K.J.O'Hagan,
Ahoghill

ACKNOWLEDGEMENTS

This book would not have been possible but for the assistance and co-operation of a great number of people to whom I am deeply indebted. The order of acknowledgement below has no bearing on the degree or amount of assistance given but is merely divided into the different groups who have contributed in different ways.

I should like, therefore, to thank the staff at the former Department of Commerce, Mineral Technology Branch, Mr Alan Smyth and Mr Geoff Warke of the Northern Ireland Geological Survey for permission to inspect and copy plans and abandonment details of the various mines, the staff at the Public Record Office, Belfast for helping me to obtain information from records of the mining companies and estate papers and the staff at the Ballymena Reference library, for their assistance in obtaining for me articles in relation to the mines from other libraries both in England and the Republic of Ireland.

In particular I should like to thank all those landowners in the Glenravel and adjoining districts for permission to tramp across their fields and hills to inspect mine levels and derelict mine buildings, notably among them Danny McCann, Dungonnell, Paddy McQuillan, Tuftarney, Roger Crawford, Parkmore, Gordon Crawford, Pollee, Hugh Thompson, formerly Rathkenny, Samuel Carlisle, Templepatrick and Hugh McCann, formerly Glenravel House. Although it's rather late now, I am especially grateful to the late Jim Montgomery, former Chief Forester at Glenariff for his frequent help and permission to enter Forestry property when I wished to examine the Parkmore and Essathohan Mines and the Glenariff Mines and railway, and for finding a temporary home for my collection of mining memorabilia in the forest park information centre for a long number of years.

Exploring disused mines is a dangerous and uncomfortable pastime and many risks were taken to explore them to the full. Such risks demand infinite care and a cool head and at times some back-breaking spadework. Experiences such as dizziness from bad air in Rathkenny Mine, swimming through ice-cold water with 3 to 5 inches of air space in Parkmore and crawling gingerly through unstable roof-falls were not enough to deter that band of followers who accompanied me on such exploratory trips. To be dragged away from the comfort of your fireside to crouch and crawl through mud and water in a cold, dark, underground maze is not the most pleasant way to spend a Sunday or any other day but to those who did, namely Patsy McGaughey, Charlie McGaughey (deceased), Kenny McGaughey, Tony Fyfe, Patrick Fyfe and Colin McIlwaine, goes a special word of thanks.

Finally, let me not forget those women who stayed behind and made no attempt to stop us but who rewarded us with huge and hearty meals on our eventual return – Patricia McGaughey, Lily McGaughey, and my own wife, Mary. Not for them the glory of discovery, only the dirty washing.

To all the above-mentioned I hope that the publication of this book will be a reward for all their help and efforts.

K J O'Hagan

Chapter One
Locations and Origins

Slievenanee

The term Ironstone is usually applied to any rock or ore which contains an appreciable quantity of iron, regardless of whether the ore occurs in veins like hematite or magnetite or in regular layers such as in the claybands and blackbands of the Ballycastle coal-measures. Thus the old 6 inch series Ordnance Survey maps of Mid and North Antrim refer to the mines as Ironstone but to distinguish them from the clayband and blackband ironstones they should be referred to as iron-ore mines since the ore they contain is in fact oxidised iron-ore of volcanic origin.

The mines to which this book relates are, therefore, iron-ore mines but with some bauxite workings. They are situated on the western and southern flanks of Slievenanee Mountain (1782ft) about 10 miles north-east of Ballymena. From Slievenanee they extend in a line almost parallel to the main road between Parkmore and a point just beyond Essathohan Bridge or the Midgey Corner, as it is more commonly called. An extensive series of long abandoned workings then continues in an arc round Trostan, Antrim's highest mountain (1817ft). These were trial workings for bauxite but were of little extent inwardly. On the other side of the road are the mines of Glenariff at the head of the glen, in the valley of its tributary the Inver River. They extend down the south side of the glen to the scarp overlooking Red bay and round the coast to the townland of Galboly Lower, due west of St Killian's College. Returning inland, another series of mines begins at Cargan village and runs through the townland of Dungonnell, then southwards along the slopes of Carncormick to Gortnageeragh. About a mile north of Cargan is the small tract of Evishacrow while westwards are the bauxite mines on the south side of Tuftarney Hill. Other bauxite and iron-ore mines can be seen on the long ridge above Newtowncrommelin. Further to the south-east are the mines of Rathkenny which form another group with those of Broughshane, namely Elginny, Ballylig, Coreen and Knockboy.

Apart from these well known mining areas there are many other locations where iron-ore has been proved. Most of the Upper Basalt outliers have been tried for ore early on in the story of mining. On the western side of Slieveanorra ore was proved at 1550 feet. On Slievenahanaghan it was found at 1100 feet, on the northern flank. Two miles north of Newtowncrommelin an outcrop is exposed over a considerable distance. On Skerry Rock both iron-ore and bauxite were proved but were of poor quality and plans to work them were abandoned.

Most of the low-lying areas between the basalt outliers have been infilled since the Ice Age by glacial debris and peat bog, at times of considerable thickness, and in such areas ore has usually only been proved where streams have cut through the surface cover to reveal traces in the stream banks. In the

Agan Burn west of the Parkmore Mines ore is exposed in this way as it is in most of the other drainage channels of the area.

Very few mineral deposits are due to present-day climatic or geological conditions; the majority are determined by geological occurrences in the distant past although in the case of the iron-ores and bauxites past climates have probably played an equally important part, as will be explained. To find the source of the Antrim iron-ores and bauxites we have to travel back in time some 60 to 65m years. Dinosaurs had become extinct and with them the Age of Reptiles was at an end. The Age of Mammals had just begun and striking changes in climate occurred which were to shape the world and make it much as we know it today.

North East Ireland then was unlike what we know it today. There were no green glens or scenic coastline. Instead the landscape was more moonlike with active volcanoes and frequent volcanic activity. The area was in fact part of a vast volcanic continent known as the Brittano-Icelandic Volcanic Province comprising N.E. Ireland, Scotland, the Hebrides, Iceland and even part of Greenland. Today the only active part of that Province is Iceland, a remnant of what conditions were like millions of years ago.

In Antrim many of the volcanoes, although long extinct, remain in part to remind us of the forces they could unleash. Names such as Slemish, Carncastle, Tiveragh, Tievebulliagh, Kenbane and Carrick-a-Rede are places of familiar scenic beauty nowadays yet these volcanoes were not in themselves responsible for the massive beds of lava which we now call the Upper and Lower Basalts. It is more likely that these outpourings were the combined result of the volcanoes along with quiet rather than explosive eruptions from ground fissures and perhaps a single huge volcano situated in what is now the North Irish Sea, somewhere between Ireland and Scotland.

Volcanic eruptions come in two basic forms – central vent eruptions, the most common kind, the kind we associate with the typical volcano, and fissure eruptions where the lava wells up through surface cracks and spreads out on each side over the land. Fissure eruptions normally occur in areas where the landmass is subjected to tensional forces. The crust simply breaks open in long vertical cracks which may remain open but deep down the magma forces its way up in a dyke. If the pressure is great enough the lava will spill out onto the surface to form a horizontal layer. Successive eruptions will build up layers hundreds of metres thick.

Iceland today is famous for its fissure eruptions and they occur continually along plate margins on the floors of the great oceans. In Antrim most of the lavas were laid down in this way, layer upon layer. These layers ranged from about six metres thick to exceptional flows of over 30 metres thick. Lava contains a high percentage of iron and aluminium. In fact, they are the two most common minerals in the Earth's crust. Being elements they cannot be broken down into anything simpler, they merely exist in the same way that oxygen exists in the air we breathe. They occur in the molten state at the Earth's core and when extruded onto the surface along with many other mineral elements they cool and solidify to form basalt.

The rocks which gave us iron-ore and bauxite were formed during a prolonged pause which interrupted the volcanic activity and this is now referred to as the Interbasaltic Period. During this period the surface of the land was subjected to the normal weathering processes of wind, rain, heat and frost and this resulted in the uppermost flows of the lower Basalt being weathered to a depth of over 50 feet in places. Lava weathers to a rich soil and during this period fertile plains and shallow lakes abounded and vegetation flourished. The Interbasaltic Period came to an end with the renewal of volcanic activity on an intensive scale and forming what we now call the Upper Basalt. This too has been severely weathered but on Trostan still attains a depth of 600 feet.

The leaching of the basalt by the chemical action of weathering removed many of the major elements of the rock but left the ores of iron and aluminium in situ in various oxide forms and for this reason they are found associated with each other in Co. Antrim . Today the red soils of the Interbasaltic Bed are known as laterites and where the oxides of aluminium predominate the laterite is called bauxite; where the oxides of iron predominate it is known as iron-ore. These laterites vary greatly not only in composition but also in appearance. Some iron-ores are mottled and streaked with lighter areas while many are dark red and even almost black. Bauxite too varies from pale grey to red and purple. Because of these colour similarities it is difficult at times to distinguish by eye between iron-ore and bauxite.

Following the complete cessation of volcanic activity the upper lava series and the interbasaltic laterite beds were removed over much of the country by the normal weathering processes and ice action and now they occur only in a

PISOLITHIC IRON ORE

FERRUGINOUS BAUXITE

(Showing Peas of Iron)

number of isolated outliers, generally on the high ground of the Antrim hills. In a few of these the iron ore and bauxite concentrations were rich enough to be of economic value.

The Interbasaltic Layer or Bed can still be plainly seen where it outcrops on the surface along the cliff path at the Giant's Causeway. Upper Basalt forms the cliffs on the south side of Glenariff Glen while those on the opposite side are Lower Basalt. The Upper Basalt dips gently inland in a continuous bed to Craigywarren and near Broughshane, including all the high ground east of the Ballymena - Waterfoot road. The other main Upper Basalt mass is that which includes Trostan and Slievenanee. A few isolated outliers occur around the village of Newtowncrommelin.

Iron ore, therefore, underlies the country from Broughshane to Trostan Mountain and probably from there to the north coast since it is seen again at the Giant's Causeway and has even been proved on Rathlin Island. Its extent may be taken as covering an area of approximately 400 square miles. Reserves in 1885 were estimated at 185 million tons but most of these were thought to be uneconomical to work when compared to cheap sources of foreign ore.

Sources:
Geological Survey of Ireland, Memoir to Sheet 14, 1886.
The Composition & Origin of the Antrim Laterites & Bauxites, HMSO, 1952.
The Geology of Ireland, Prof J K Charlesworth, 1953.
A World Survey, Vol III, J F Unstead, University of London Press Ltd., reprinted 1961.

Slemish mountain

Tievebulliagh

Giant's Causeway

The Mountains of Iron

Chapter Two
History of Mining

Parkmore Miners
(photo: Antrim Iron Ore Co)

Iron was mined at various locations in Ireland, notably in the south east, as far back as the early 1600's and in the north many bloomeries sprang up to smelt ores imported from Lancashire using wood charcoal which was obtainable from the abundant woods and forests which covered the country. Many of the works and furnaces were destroyed during the troubles of 1641 and following years. In Ulster some survived, and before the end of the century there were even some new ones, but with the decimation and destruction of the forests wood became so scarce that the manufacture of iron ceased.

Prior to the mining of iron-ore in the Glenravel area the only known source of iron in this part of the country was from the Blackband and Clayband Ironstones of the Ballycastle Coalfield[1] which were exported to Scotland. The coal mines here are probably the oldest in Ireland, having been worked as far back as the 14th century. It is known that the English opened a lead mine in Co. Antrim some time before 1641 but the location of this mine which yielded one pound of silver to every 30lbs of lead is quite unknown. There is also evidence of copper and lead being proved on Slieveanorra – the mountain of gold, and gold can still be found in the Glendun river – but no records of workings or of the exact location of these finds remain.

It could be said that Slievenanee Mountain was the hub of the mining industry in Glenravel when mining became established. No other mountain in the area is so conspicuous and no other mountain was so extensively mined. It contains a vast honeycomb of underground workings. The name of the mountain itself could not be more fitting for it was apparently known on old maps as Slieve an Eerin (Sliabh an Iarainn), the mountain of iron, and suggests that the early inhabitants knew of the existence of iron. Early surveyors too were aware of errors in their compass readings which suggested the presence of a large mass of iron. However, this knowledge was not utilised and no attempt was made to find or work the ore before the coming of the 19th century.[2]

Up to the early 1800's the poor people of the area lived mainly on what they were able to provide themselves from their small holdings, namely milk, butter and the little corn they were able to harvest. This was supplemented to a large extent by potatoes which were a more easily cultivated crop. The linen industry had led to the growing of flax, the spinning and weaving of linen yarn and cloth – a home industry - and there was also some production of pork for the market in Ballymena. The people were able to obtain cheap fuel from the plentiful peat deposits covering the hill slopes but housing conditions themselves were very poor and rents high. The only roads were from Clogh to Cushendall via what is now known as the 'Green Road' at Parkmore and the one from Skerry over Glens Brae. Other roads were only mere tracks.

About this time Nicholas Delacherois Crommelin came to Skerry Ravel (now Skerry East and Skerry West) with a colony of Protestant settlers. He was a great grand nephew of the famous Louis Crommelin, the Huguenot who had founded the linen industry near Lisburn, and he commenced a scheme of improvements and a building programme which can be seen to this day. His first task was to reclaim a lot of the barren mountain land for farming. He then set about making a new road from Skerry to Cushendun over Orra, built a church, meeting house and schools for the new population and constructed the village which now bears his name.

The settlers, however, found the land too poor and the winter climate too harsh and many soon abandoned their farms leaving Skerry Ravel with the unusual title – Scare the Devil[3].

In 1843, still trying to improve conditions for the local people, Crommelin discovered some red rock in the area and took it to Mr. John F. Hodges for examination. Hodges, who five years later was to be appointed Professor of Chemistry at Queen's College (now the University), described it as 'a reddish coloured, somewhat soft rock containing between 18 and 25% peroxide of iron'. Crommelin was enthusiastic with this analysis and by 1844 had built himself a small furnace to smelt this new-found ore using the local peat for firing. He succeeded in producing some metallic iron and the inner walls of his furnace bear testimony to his attempts in the form of melted stonework.

The use of turf for smelting was nothing new for it had been used in Sweden, Russia and the continent extensively and with great success. Iron which is smelted using coal retains impurities in the final pig-iron product, thus reducing its strength, but it was found that iron smelted using turf or turf charcoal is much superior in quality. In Germany, clayband ironstone was smelted using air-dried turf with very good results.[4] It is reasonable to assume, therefore, that Crommelin's attempts would have been successful even with medium-grade iron ore. However, due to enormous difficulties, both in materials and workers, and especially in obtaining regular supplies of air-dried turf in an area of frequent rain and heavy snow, he finally abandoned the experiment, unaware that much richer ores existed in the area. His primitive foundry still stands beside the Skerry Water, near the village of Newtown-crommelin, a monument to his endeavours.

Crommelin's Furnace
◄

Glenravel House
►

A few years later the first failure of the potato crop occurred followed by the famine of 1847 and this probably overshadowed any further interest in iron ore.

Some years earlier the Benns had come to Glenravel where they built Binvore Cottage (formerly known as Glenravel Cottage) in 1836 and then moved to the larger country mansion of Glenravel House which John Benn, the father, built in 1842 and where he died in 1853. Around this time other industries began to flourish, mainly due to the enterprise of Edward Benn, of charitable institution fame. Notable among these was the building of a distillery at Evishacrow for the distillation of alcohol from potatoes, a business which succeeded for a short time up to and including the famine years but which was brought to an end by the inclusion of a single, vital word in the relevant Act of Parliament which gave it an air of illegality and enabled the Excise authorities to put a stop to the endeavour.

The next experiment to be attempted was perhaps Glenravel's one and only claim to fame, if fame it can be called since it is virtually unknown. Its object was to produce paraffin and other substances from the rich bituminous peat of the area and to this end a furnace was built in 1850 for the distillation process. It should be noted that prior to this the existence of paraffin was unknown except in laboratory specimens and it could be said, therefore, that the peat bogs of the Glenravel mountains gave birth to that common, everyday commodity we know so well. The experiment attracted worldwide interest and the Glenravel works were subsequently transferred to the Bog of Allen for commercial working. However, the peat there proved inferior for the purpose and at about the same time new sources of paraffin were discovered from oil and shale and other natural reserves. So this experiment too was doomed.

On the death of his father Edward Benn became the new Glenravel landlord and began to carry out improvements on the estate, draining the poorer areas to increase farmland and planting trees and hedges. He built a school at Craigdunloof which has now been replaced by a bungalow. The plantation at Glenravel House dates from this time as does the present Ballymena - Cushendall road which runs through it. Benn gave instructions to his tenants to preserve samples of the different types of stones or other unusual material found which were to be brought to him. Perhaps this was because both he and his brother George had an interest in antiquities but at any rate it resulted in him coming into the possession about 1854 of a sample of red ore. This was then shown to a Dr. Buchan, a Scotsman, who was so impressed he offered Benn 10 shillings per ton of this ore. On hearing this Benn had his ore smelted by one of his own tenants, John McAlister of Legagrane, a blacksmith, who managed to produce a small pig of iron. This was then taken to Rowan's foundry in Belfast where it was made into nails and identified as having been produced from the best Swedish ore. This was praise indeed and it was left to Pat Doran, an itinerant but expert mineral collector, known as Diamond Pat, to locate the source of the rich ore which he did on Slievenanee. He presented Benn with some large specimens but Benn was unable to get the well-known ironworkers interested in mining the ore and again for some years the discovery was left unexploited. It wasn't until the arrival of James Fisher on the scene that mining the ore became a serious proposition.

In 1862 James Fisher came to live at Cleggan Lodge at Aughafatten. This house and the lands of over 1600 acres had formerly belonged to the O'Neill estate but passed through Dr. Colville's descendants to the Earl of Mountcashel and were eventually sold in 1851 by the Commissioners of Encumbered Estates to Mr. J O'Hara of Ballymena[5]. Griffith's primary valuation (1861) shows it as being held by Thomas Fisher, an older brother of James. However, Thomas went bankrupt and James subsequently bought Cleggan Lodge and 1500 acres of land for £10,000 in May 1862 and it became his principle residence, removing to it with his family from Barrow-in-Furness. Fisher had started his working life in agriculture and owned a grocer's shop. He became Barrow's first postmaster in 1847 and by 1848 had started to buy shares in ships. He then became an iron ore agent for a large mining concern and by 1858 was able to buy his own ships and sold shares in them. It was his brother's bankruptcy which brought him to Ireland and to Cleggan where he was aptly located for what was to follow.

Credit for the initiation of mining in the area is traditionally given to the parish priest of the time, the Rev. William John MacAuley. However, in February 1867 Professor Hodges disputed this, stating that he had examined the samples found by Pat Doran and that this was the first real examination of the

James Fisher

rich Glenravel ores. Perhaps he felt that the glory of discovery should go to himself but, as stated above, nothing came of it until James Fisher arrived at Cleggan. Fr. MacAuley had been born in Ballymena and ordained in 1849 and served in the Glenravel parish from 1856 to 1878. He was aware that the home-based linen industry, by which the majority of his parishioners lived, was in decline owing to the rise of the large spinning mills in neighbouring towns and this would inevitably have led to even greater poverty. His parish included the Braid and no doubt because of this he became acquainted with James Fisher of Cleggan, just across the road from the church. When a parishioner showed Fr. MacAuley a piece of red rock he had found Fisher was immediately contacted for no doubt the priest was aware of his background. They both set off on an exploration trip to Ballynahavla on the slopes of Slievenanee, accompanied by the man who found the sample and one other. Although he was a keen rambler and interested in geology Fr. MacAuley did not actually join in the search for the ore for he was a man of between 16 and 20st and on this occasion felt more inclined to lie back and take in the fresh mountain air. The others proceeded to look for the origin of the red rock and went almost directly to the spot. Lifting back a piece of overhanging turf they discovered a seam nearly two feet thick.

Fisher and the priest at once proceeded to Glenravel House to see Edward Benn who, being well acquainted with the significance of the find and Fisher's plans, decided that here was an opportunity of giving employment to the poor people on his estate and of encouraging an influx of new tenants into it which in turn meant more rent. He gave Fisher permission to dig for six months at a rent of £10 to see how things went.

The agreement (see page 32) was dated 1.11.1866 and read as follows:-
"I agree to accept the nominal sum of £10 for the liberty of removing off the land as much ore as you choose until the 1st of May 1867, this agreement to cease on that day; I consider we are both in the dark on this subject: it is very probable that after you have worked a month you will see so much as to induce you to enter into a permanent agreement, or find out that it is not worth following; this I will say that I will be most willing that you should have a good thing, & although we would be on 1st May, as we are now, both free, we will know a good deal more about it. You of course will know more than I could be expected to know."[6]

In 1866 therefore Fisher began opencast mining at a place known as the Gullets on the slopes of Slievenanee where the ore was conveniently situated close to the surface and in those first six months was able to ship 18,000 tons of ore to England worth about £1 per ton. By this time he had founded the company, James Fisher & Sons which still bears his name today, and realised that more and better ore lay below the ground and had already driven adits to work it. The first underground mine to be opened was aptly named the Glenravel Mine, situated in the townland of Legegrane close to the Gullets. This was in January or February 1867. An account of its opening was given in the Ballymena Observer, Saturday 25.7.1868:

The Iron Mine of Glenravil.

"Within the last two years an extensive and valuable iron mine was discovered at Glenravil about 7 miles from Ballymena by James Fisher Esq. of Cleggan Lodge near this town and of Barrow -in- Furness, Lancashire. Under the energetic management of this enterprising gentleman it was opened about 18 months ago. It has given constant employment to 80 workmen, and we are happy to say that it is now yielding 300 tons per week of the purest magnetic, hematite iron ore, giving an analysis of about 60% metallic iron and also a considerable proportion of manganese and titanium, the ore conveyed from the mine for a distance of two miles by a tramway constructed by Mr. Fisher; and it is from thence carted six miles along a good road to the harbour of Red Bay near Cushendall, where vessels of moderate tonnage can get in and out at all tides. And from this port large shipments of the ore have already been made to England, Wales and Scotland where its quality is highly appreciated and the demand for it is rapidly upon the increase.

The opening of this important mine and tramway was celebrated at Glenravil on the 3rd inst. upon which occasion about fifty gentlemen chiefly from the town and neighbourhood of Ballymena were entertained at a recherche collation provided by Mr. Fisher on the adjacent mountain.

There is every reason for hope that the ore of the Glenravil Mine will command a ready and extensive sale in the English markets, any quantity of it can be raised at a moderate outlay and we cordially wish prosperity to this and every other effort to develop the industrial resources of our native country".

Fisher continued to open fresh adits all along the hillside including the Ballynahavla Pit near the terminus of his tramway. He still had interests in Barrow and had taken over a ship repair yard there and had begun to build his own sailing ships. He extended his lease from Benn from August 1868 for 20 years at £300 p.a. which was later superseded in November 1871 at £400 p.a. for 31 years. By 1872 he owned 80 ships. Following his death in 1873 at 50 years of age from a stroke, his son John purchased his father's interest in the lease for 16 years from December 1877 at £300 p.a.

James Fisher's initial success in the mines did not go unnoticed and soon the Antrim Iron Ore Co., the Evishacrow Iron Ore Co., the Crommelin Mining Co., and Parkmore Iron Ore Company, to name but a few, commenced mining operations. The formation of the Antrim Iron Ore Co. was described in detail in the Ballymena Observer of 27th January 1872, as follows :

The Antrim Iron Ore Company

The above company is now in process of formation, under the most favourable circumstances, and with very hopeful prospects of early and permanent success. Its object is to develop the mineral treasures of our County, and for such operations it has been ascertained, beyond all doubt, that there is a rich and ample field.

The mining rights of the Company extend over 40,000 acres of County Antrim, containing an incalculable quantity of iron ore; and millions of tons are in localities from which shipments may conveniently be made at the ports and harbours of Belfast, Carrickfergus, Larne, Glenarm, Carnlough, Red Bay, Ballintoy, and Portrush. From six mines, already opened and in which 170 men are at present employed, the weekly product, obtained with comparatively little labour, is about 1,200 tons. Six other mines will be opened immediately; and there is every reason for belief that the shipments of the present year will amount to 120,000 tons, whilst in 1873 it may be fairly anticipated that the produce will be doubled.

The ore is of a very superior quality. It has been found suitable for conversion into steel, and there is an unlimited demand for it in England. Under these auspicious circumstances the undertaking presents a very promising opportunity for the safe as well as highly remunerative investment of unoccupied money; and the directors of the Company are well known as gentlemen of high character and much business experience, in whose discretion the community may have unbounded confidence.

The Company is organised under the Limited Liabilities' Acts of '62 and '67. Its capital will be £100,000, in 20,000 shares of £5 each; but the first issue will be limited to 10,000 shares. A deposit of 10s. per share will be required on application, and 10s. more upon allotment. Subsequent calls are not to exceed £1 per share, and at intervals of not less than three months. Of the first issue eight thousand shares have already been taken up and only two thousand remain for disposal to applicants.

Further particulars will be found in a prospectus which will be submitted for the consideration of our readers at an early day. We understand that portions of the Ballymena district will come under the mining operations of the Company; and we earnestly hope that an undertaking so praiseworthy and patriotic will result in merited prosperity to all concerned in it.

With several mining companies now in operation, there was a great influx of people into the area as Benn had anticipated and the villages of Fisherstown[7] (named after James Fisher), Rathkenny, Newtowncrommelin and Parkmore sprang up or were extended and many small, stone, mountain houses were hurriedly built, scattered over the area. Since mining in those days was mostly pick and shovel work, any farmer or farm labourer could do it and they found new employment with better rates of pay and soon acquired the other skills of mining. Most of the miners in fact were labourers and small farmers and the owner of a small farm could even do part-time work at the mines when farming conditions permitted. This helped to supplement his modest farm income. Between 1867 and 1875 wages rose from 12/- a week to 15 and 20/- a week for underground workers and from 7/6 to 14/- a week for surface workers. In 1873 there were about 700 men employed directly in the mines and 600 horses were engaged in carting away the ore to Red Bay. It was reckoned that the mining companies were spending close on £80,000 per annum in wages and freight which by today's standards is equivalent to several millions.

To the ordinary farm worker the meaning of this newfound source of wealth can best be illustrated by the following extract from a letter to the Ballymena Observer dated 15th November 1873:

"Sir,
 Allow me to state a few opinions which, I think, will do no harm to the cause which you have so ably advocated. From my own personal experience, first of all, I may inform your readers, that, as a miner, I have (thanks to Mining Enterprise in this County) raised myself above the drudgery of farm labour, in which I toiled, 4 years ago, 12 hours per day, on hire of 5/- per week, with a moderate diet of country fare, where beef or mutton was never seen except when grazing in the fields. I am now able to clear 25/- per week, working only 8 hours per day, and can afford to come into Ballymena each fortnightly pay and purchase my provisions and clothing without being imposed upon by the small country dealers; and can also afford to take home with me a decent wedge of that now precious commodity 'Beef" upon which, allow me to state, according to the present prices of cattle, you Ballymena butchers exact too much profit."

This new source of wealth for the miners led to a rather unruly sort of life and drinking sprees and brawls were common. Fisherstown was so wild at times that children were not allowed on the street when the miners were in town – a situation more akin to the Wild West in the days of the gold rush.

By the early 1870's, therefore, several mines were being worked on both sides of the valley between Martinstown and Parkmore and by 1873 mining had begun in an extensive area at the head of Glenariff Glen. A few years later mining was under way to the south at Rathkenny and around Broughshane.

Up to 1872 the mines had been worked solely for iron ore. Aluminium was still a virtually unknown commodity and it was only in 1870 that it was realised it could be obtained from bauxite. The electrolytic process for the separation of aluminium from bauxite, discovered in 1854 but scrapped due to high costs, was re-invented in the late 1880s almost simultaneously in France and USA.[8] It was not until 1886 that aluminium could be produced on a practical, commercial basis. It was Professor Hodges again who, probably because of his familiarity with the ores of the district, discovered bauxite in the Cargan Mine in 1871 and this discovery added more interest and potential to the mining industry and boosted output for several years. During these years too the narrow gauge railway had arrived, reaching Fisherstown in 1875 and Parkmore in late 1876. Branch lines were laid to the various groups of mines and these facilitated the ore being removed quickly from the mines to Ballymena and thence to Larne for shipment. Mining then, even as today, was dependent on an efficient means of getting the ore away quickly. The railways encouraged expansion in the mining industry and made the ore more valuable because it was more accessible.

However, in the early 1880s the industry started to decline owing to a slump in the iron industry in Britain and the exhaustion of the better class ores although other factors contributed as well. By 1883 there were 435 miners still employed and the following year only 343. The number of miners continued to decline steadily after this. The production of bauxite continued and some mines went over completely to the mining of bauxite e.g. Tuftarney and Evishacrow Mines, the latter being worked up to 1926 when less than 100 men were engaged in mining. Iron ore production carried on at reduced pace in most of the mines and towards the turn of the Century the Crommelin company even opened a series of new mines along the east side of the Skerry Water and two bauxite mines on the west side. In general, however, the number of working adits steadily declined and desperate efforts were sometimes called for to prolong mining, namely driving costly tunnels for drainage or boring through dykes.

The question as to whether the iron-ore could be smelted locally was considered as far back as 1873 by utilising the vast peat resources of the area as a cheap source of fuel. Works were set up in Glenravel on bogland owned by Mr. Benn to pulp the peat and turn it into peat briquettes. The operation was run by the Ulster Peat Company but the difficulty of drying the bricks in open sheds all the year round proved slow and unprofitable due to the heavy annual rainfall and the scheme and the idea of a smelter were abandoned. It is interesting to note that the Braidwater Spinning Company, Ballymena, contributed £110 towards the endeavour. Incidentally, the last place in Ireland where iron was smelted was at the Creevelea Iron Works, in Co. Roscommon (from a photograph of the works in 1905).

In 1874 a prophetic writer, R.A. Watson, in an article in the Dublin University Magazine, made the comment that it would take some hundreds of years before these ore deposits would become exhausted but sadly prophecy and actuality are seldom one and the same. All mining enterprises have to be abandoned sooner or later either because the deposits are exhausted or their extraction no longer pays. Mining, therefore, must eventually disappear from any area since it is only a temporary form of occupation[9] and the miners have to revert to other types of employment if this is available. So it was that the closure of the mines reversed the employment situation with many of the miners going back to farm labour or seeking new jobs.

However, although the mining industry in Antrim appeared to have died prematurely it had not been forgotten and its finest hour was yet to come. With the outbreak of World War Two a new and sinister crisis loomed in the shape of U-boats and it became increasingly difficult to obtain foreign bauxite. In 1940 Lord Beaverbrook advised the nation of the scarcity of aluminium and aluminium was a vital ingredient in the manufacture of warplanes. By this time Germany was producing about 50% more aluminium than the USA because of her control of aluminium-producing countries. So it was that interest in the Antrim bauxites was rekindled and this led to a re-investigation of local reserves. In 1941 new bauxite mines were opened at Newtowncrommelin, known as the Skerry mines, and at Templepatrick. Other abandoned workings were re-opened for their bauxite content and many Glenravel miners or sons of miners were recruited to work in the new mines. The Skerry Mines closed early in 1944 and mining as an industry finally ceased on 31-12-45 with the closure of Lyle's Hill and Ballynabarnish Mines. Since then there has been no further working. In all, about 296,000 tons of bauxite were removed during World war II and this was treated at Larne to remove the ferrous content.

Cleggan House

Spoil Heaps (the Bings) Slievenanee

All that remains now are the little disused railway tracks, the spoil heaps and the mine levels, some open, though gated, some closed and some with no visible trace, the ruined windlass above Cargan and numerous derelict buildings connected with the industry. Although vast reserves of low-grade iron ore and bauxite still remain it is improbable that the mines will ever be worked again as mining of these could not compete with opencast production in other countries.

Sources:
1. Irish Geography, 1973, Vol VI, No.5, K L Wallwork.
2. Presidential address to Belfast Natural History & Philosophical Society, Prof. JFW Hodges, 1875.
3. The Parish of Glenravel, Rev J Smith, Down & Connor Historical Society's Journal, Vol 10, 1939.
4. The Industrial Resources of Ireland, Robert Kane, 1845.
5. Diocese of Down & Connor, Rev J O'Laverty, 1884.
6. Original Fisher/Benn Agreement, Author's possession.
7. The name Fisherstown eventually passed away but remained for a hundred years on the school which Fr. MacAuley had built in 1875 and to which John Fisher had been a generous benefactor, his father James having died in 1873. Fr. MacAuley had also laid the foundation stone of Lignamonagh school but died before it was completed. His death, in 1878, was deeply mourned especially by the miners themselves who never forgot what he had done for them. As a mark of their reverence for him they dug his grave with their own hands, lined it with stone and tiled the bottom. Then they covered it with oak timbers from the church roof which had been replaced with iron girders3 (the church was destroyed by a bomb in 1972). He was the third parish priest of Glenravel to be buried in the parish graveyard. Fr MacAuley in life had remained a warm friend of the Fisher family and the whole of the mine owners liberally subscribed towards the erection in Glenravel of a large Celtic cross to his memory (see John Fisher's biography, Appx 12).
8. http://59.1911encyclopedia.org/A/AL/ALUMINIUM.htm.
9. A World Survey, Vol III, J F Unstead, University of London Press Ltd., reprinted 1961.

The agreement written between James Fisher and Edward Benn

I agree to accept the nominal sum of £10 for the liberty of removing off the land as much ore as you choose until the 1 May 67, this agreement to cease on that day; I consider we are both in the dark on this subject: it is very probable that after you have worked a month you will see so much as to induce you to enter into a permanent agreement, or find out that it is not worth following, this I will say that I will be most willing that you sd have a good thing, & although we sd be on the 1 May as we are now both free, we will know a good deal more about it, for if come will know more than I could be expected to know.

Edwd Benn

Glenravel 1 Nov 1866

Mr Jas Fisher
Glasgow

Chapter Three
The Benn Family

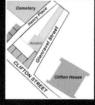

Clockwise from top left: Edward Benn; Benn's Planting; Edward Benn's headstone; the arches at Samaritan Hospital; a plan showing the location of Benn's hospital; the inscription on plaque at Binvore Cottage

THE BENEFACTORS

To the people of Belfast the Benn family is mainly associated with endowments and good works and ample generosity and is commemorated in those institutions in Belfast of which they were benefactors. The main benefactor of the family was Edward Benn and the building to which he is most often linked is Clifton House where the two wings were endowed by him in 1872. The plaques, one on each wing, show the details and unlike other plaques which bear his name, state his address as Glenravel House. At the rear of Clifton House is Glenravel Street, named after the country estate where the Benns were landlords. It was here that the Belfast Hospital for Diseases of the Skin was erected in 1873 at a cost of £3,300, all at Edward Benn's expence. This facility had previously been in Regent Street but became unsuitable for its purpose owing to the large numbers of patients seeking treatment. Glenravel Street Hospital was state of the art for its time, with the most up-to-date equipment and facilities. It is believed that free treatment was available there to any patient from Glenravel who needed it. During the Belfast blitz of 1941 the building was extensively damaged and could not be restored to its original state so, thereafter, treatment was provided at the Royal Victoria where it remains to this day.

Next was the Ulster Eye, Ear & Throat Hospital which was endowed in 1874. Others were the Samaritan Hospital, Lisburn Road, and the Royal Belfast Academical Institution (Inst) which George Benn contributed to. He had been a student there in his younger days and wrote his first History of the Town of Belfast while there in 1823. It is for this, and his later histories, that he is best remembered although both he and Edward had antiquarian interests as well and Edward's collection formed a substantial basis to the Old Museum building in College Square North. But many people, including academics, are unaware of their life outside the metropolis as landlords of a large estate in Glenravel. The family features in an important respect in the history of Glenravel and the mining industry but after the beginnings of the industry, not in a major role. After all, the Benns were merely landlords of a mountainous area of poor land, situated on the edge of the Antrim Plateau, sparsely inhabited when they arrived on the scene and only suitable for sheep, a few cows and for turf. Fortunately for the Benns and their tenants and indirectly for Belfast, it became the centre of an industry which spread throughout most of North, East and Mid-Antrim, providing hundreds of jobs and a higher standard of living which could not have been foreseen when the Benn family first took up residence.

The Mountains of Iron

THE EARLY YEARS

The name Benn first appears in Ireland in 1750 and may be of Huguenot origin. John Benn, born in Whitehaven, Cumbria in 1721, settled in the Newry area in 1750 where he was engaged as engineer on the Newry Canal. He had three sons – Edward, Thomas and John, the latter being born in 1767. This John married Elizabeth Craig from Tandragee where they set up home and started their family. They moved to Belfast in the early 1800's where John opened a brewery in North Street which was operating in 1819. They had nine children of whom Edward and George are the most famous. The family moved to Hercules Street and then No.4 College Square North but in 1836 when John was 69 years of age we find the name in Glenravel. It is known that following in their father's footsteps, the brothers Edward and George had also been engaged in the brewing trade in Downpatrick and had probably made sufficient money from this business to purchase the Glenravel estate comprising nearly 3,500 acres in the mid-1830's and to bring their father, now retired, with them. Perhaps John's health was failing and this was to get him out of the smoke and grime of the city into fresh mountain air or perhaps the brothers had other business plans (see below).

AT GLENRAVEL

Their first residence in Glenravel, built in 1836, was known as Binvore Cottage, situated beside the Binvore Burn in the townland of Evishacrow. But in 1842 John built a much grander residence just a short distance away called Glenravel House. A description of the house was given by one of the servants who worked in the house in the 1950s. Although this was a hundred years after the house was built it's likely that the house hadn't changed that much in its layout.

"Downstairs there was a drawing room, dining room, hall, china pantry, kitchen, gun room, milk parlour containing churns and milk cans, and a room for the dogs in which they were fed. On the second floor was an attic in which the maids used to live in years gone by, but that was well before my time. On the first floor they had a bedroom and adjoining dressing room — which was really like a walk-in wardrobe, they also had a sitting room, which was close to their bedroom. There was also a writing room, which was a kind of office with a lot of shelves of books. There were three other bedrooms which were fully furnished and used only for visitors. There was also a bathroom, and a hot-press room, which had high piles of freshly-starched sheets".

John Benn died there in March 1853. It is likely that Edward continued to live at Binvore Cottage until his father's death for three reasons:

1. Binvore Cottage was only six years old in 1842.
2. The Census records for 1851 do not show Edward or George living with the parents and siblings. By the next census date John was dead so it's fortunate that this record has survived .
3. Benn's distillery was just across the field from Binvore Cottage and not convenient to Glenravel House.

THE DISTILLERY

It was during these early years in Glenravel that events occurred which were to have lasting memories and consequences both in Glenravel and Belfast. Having been brought up in the brewing business it was natural that Edward, who was the most business-minded of the two brothers, should seek to continue in that trade. He built a distillery close to Binvore Cottage, at a cost of £2,000, where he succeeded in distilling whiskey from potatoes which his tenants were encouraged to grow for a small fee on small hilly fields. He had about 64 tenants at the time. This was just prior to the Great Famine which was later to devastate most of Ireland. The considerable waste from the process was fed to pigs and cattle and the land was improved for further cultivation of other crops. However, the Excise Authorities had their eye on the proceedings and due to the inclusion of a single, vital word in the relevant Act of Parliament which gave it an air of illegality, it enabled the Excisemen to put a stop to the endeavour after just a few years of operation. In fact, to help with fermentation Benn had added a small amount of barley and to the authorities this was the same as operating an illegal still. Benn was fined £100 and the distillery was left to go to ruin. He was of course furious, for his £2,000 was down the drain, and he penned a sharp letter to Lord John Russell , the then Prime Minister –

"I am grieved when I consider that when I had conquered a stubborn soil and an ignorant people I found in the Commissioners a more powerful and more dangerous enemy ...".

Both he and George went to Liverpool where they established another brewing business for a time before returning to Co. Antrim.

During its lifetime the distillery produced about 100 puncheons of whiskey which, in the words of a local tenant, James McCann, "tasted all right" (a puncheon was a large cask which held 120 gallons).

IMPROVEMENTS

His reference to an ignorant people was an indication of how he treated his tenants. Despite his reputation later as a charitable benefactor and philanthropist he was not as charitable to his tenants. He was, in fact, the opposite as were the other members of his family. He encouraged his tenants to improve their holdings but he did not support Ulster Tenant Right whereby tenants who disposed of their holdings were entitled to compensation for any improvements they had carried out. On the contrary, when they improved their farms he merely increased their rents. He gave little credit to his tenants for any improvements carried out by them. In fact, he himself took the credit for most of the work done as is evidenced by an account of the estate written by himself.

"Very little drainage is required here, what has been done was done by me. Some fences have been made by the tenants, but for the most part by me, a good many with gates having been put up by me. All the planting has been done by me, in some cases a few old trees are found around the old houses.

"From this it will be seen that all improvements made by tenants scarcely merit the name, but they nearly all hold by lease for 31 years; a few from year to year. They would not be permitted to sell their farms. Improvements are going on but not as much as should be. Their rents are well paid, the land is let a good deal above the valuation and the tenantry generally prosperous. Notices to quit are not given.

"What you call Ulster Tenant Right exists to a considerable extent in the district. I do not admit it on this property; it is ruinous to all concerned. In many cases the farms are worse off than when they were taken, the seller being often a lazy, unimproving man".

TREATMENT OF TENANTRY

Up to the early 1800s the poor people of the area lived mainly on what they were able to provide themselves from their small holdings, namely milk, butter and the little corn they were able to harvest. This was supplemented to a large extent by potatoes which were a more easily cultivated crop. The linen industry had led to the growing of flax, the spinning and weaving of linen yarn and cloth – a home industry – and there was also some production of pork for the market in Ballymena. The people were able to obtain cheap fuel from the plentiful peat deposits covering the hill slopes but housing conditions themselves were very poor and rents high. There were no decent roads, only mere tracks. For the small farmers who made up the bulk of the inhabitants on his estate life was never easy. He likened them to low animals which if you flung them into a ditch would struggle to get to the top of the bank again. So his tenants always had to struggle to keep their heads above water, to feed and rear their families and spend their days toiling in the fields. Despite Benn's so-called improvements to their farms the tenants had little good to say about any of the Benns. The family was described as heartless and tyrannical and stories have come down through the years to the descendants of those tenants who were treated badly, of evictions in Winter, unjust rent increases and of Miss Harriet Benn deliberately pouring buttermilk down the drain rather than give it to poor families to feed their children.

ATTEMPT ON BENN'S LIFE

Little wonder then that on 26th July 1858 an attempt was made on the life of Edward Benn by firing a shot through the bedroom window. However, it was actually George who was standing at the window closing the shutters with a candle in his hand. The assailant missed his target and ran off, disappearing into the mountains among people who had no love for either of the brothers and was never captured. An account of the attack was published in the Ballymena Observer newspaper on the 7th August that year, referring to the intended victim as Edward Benn but a reward notice correctly refers to the victim as George.

DISCOVERY OF IRON ORE

The extraction of the iron ores which were discovered on Benn's estate has already been referred to. Suffice to say that the Benns themselves did not actually own or work any mines. Other miners from further afield flooded into the area until soon there were 700 men and 300 horses and all the subsidiary trades that they needed – blacksmiths, carpenters, carters, stone masons etc – working on the hills of Benn's estate. All these people needed accommodation and Fisher and other companies provided houses for them. With this increase in tenants and mining companies Edward Benn was now receiving increased payments from rents and royalties. Little wonder then that he could well afford to be charitable to those Belfast institutions which today commemorate him. However, both Benn and Fisher did not live long enough to witness the decline which was to follow in the 1880's. Fisher died in 1873 and Edward Benn in 1874 and he was succeeded by his brother George as landlord. By 1875 the narrow gauge railway from Ballymena had been laid through the Benn estate to transport the ore and this too was a further source of revenue for the new landlord.

Edward himself saw little of the effects of his generosity to Belfast. For seven years prior to his death he hadn't even visited Belfast but on his decease his body was brought to Belfast and interred in Clifton Street burying ground. Perhaps it's just as well for if he had been interred in Glenravel it is doubtful if he would have been allowed to 'rest in peace'.

GEORGE BENN & AFTER

George Benn had lived a retired life at Glenravel House for more than 30 years and it was there he had written the greater part of his two-volume History of Belfast published in 1877 and 1880. On the death of his brother, he moved to Belfast where he resided initially at Derryvolgie Avenue but a year later he had bought a house at Fortwilliam Park where he was joined by his three unmarried sisters. In the meantime Glenravel House was let to John Fisher, who was now owner of the Glenravel Mines following the death of his father, James. George continued to manage the Glenravel Estate from Fortwilliam and there are two letters written to him in September 1881 by the secretary of the Antrim Iron Ore Company which was working the Cargan Mines. The company was struggling to keep going and was seeking a reduction in rent to avoid having to lay off miners. George was in failing health and nearly blind and this was only three and a half months before his death in January 1882. What Benn's response was or if the rent was reduced or not is not known but in 1882 the Cargan Mines were taken over by the Crommelin Mining Company who continued to work them for several years. On his death in 1882 he left £1,000 to the Belfast Charitable Society to provide a special dinner for the residents of Clifton House every Christmas and Easter. It wasn't till January 1884 that Glenravel House was put up for auction. It was sold to Professor John F W Hodges who had married Elizabeth Benn, a sister of the Benn brothers. It was Hodges who had analysed the first iron ore samples found by Nicholas Crommelin in Glenravel in 1843 and who had identified the first occurrence of bauxite in the British Isles, at the Cargan Mines in 1871. He had also been the first president of the Belfast Hospital for Diseases of the Skin at Glenravel Street. At Glenravel House he set up his own private experimental agricultural station where he carried out research into flax, manures and silage. After his death in 1899, and that of his elder son killed at the Somme, the house was inhabited by his younger son, Captain Jack Hodges, a champion boxer, golfer, and drinker, who lived on there with his first and second wives until his death in 1970.

The Drum Brae at Evishacrow showing Lazy Beds and Distilley
◄

Map of the original Benn estate land in Glenravel
►

THE BENN ESTATE
GLENRAVEL
LEGAGRANE
EVISHACROW
CARGAN
DUNGONNELL
CRAIGDUNLOOF

CONCLUSION

Over the past 30 years or so many new housing estates have been built in the Glenravel area but there is no church, school, monument or plaque to the Benn name. The nearest there is, is an estate called Benvore Park, spelt with one N, in Cargan, which is a combination of Binvore and supposedly Benn. The plantation which Edward Benn laid out still bears the name of Benn's Plantin' and has been the scene over many years of several ghostly occurrences. Many stories have been told over the years relating to the ghost of George Benn haunting the roads around Glenravel House, stories of a man in black hat and long-tailed coat being seen, of horses which refused to pass the big house, of strange unexplained occurrences and apparitions whilst driving along the road late at night, of the spirit of George Benn sealed in a bottle and buried below the doorstep. The reader may think these stories are mere fairy tales and, with the passing of time and the demise of the older generation, the stories too are alluded to less and less, but they are an indication of how the Benn family was regarded and, with some people in the area today, still is regarded.

Glenravel House today has been nearly totally demolished. In time it too will be no more and along with it will go, perhaps, the spirit in the bottle below the doorstep. Maybe then the reputation of the Benns of Glenravel will also be laid to rest.

Sources:
History of Dermatology in N.Ireland, Reginald Hall, RVH, 1970.
The Evishacro Distillery, Hugh McQuillan, Ballymena Guardian, 8/8/1974.
Two Faces of the Benns, Fred Heatley, Northern Life Vol 3, 1982.
The Benn family of Belfast and Glenravel, Fred Heatley, Ulster Local Studies Vols 5 & 6, 1980.
Glenravel, A Local History, Glenravel Community Association, 1993.

Chapter Four
The Economic Aspect

Miners' Row, Parkmore

The advent of the mining industry to North East Antrim brought about the opening up of one of the most barren and inhospitable areas in the country. Like all mining ventures, however, decline is inevitable since minerals which have been removed from the Earth's crust do not regenerate and often what was once a thriving industrial community becomes a ghost town, for example, in the American West and in parts of Cornwall. In other cases the population remains and survives by reverting to other forms of employment mainly farming, while the younger generation seeks employment in the towns and cities. This is the situation in the Glenravel area today.

At the beginning Fisher's success was the spark which set the mining industry on its feet. It brought new employment and new skills to the area and an opportunity to earn more money. Those who came to mining from other types of occupation quickly adapted to the change and it was reckoned that a farm labourer could become a skilled miner in three months. However, apart from the job of actually mining ore underground there was a great demand for all types of worker, craftsman and labourer alike. The mine owner's aim was to get the ore to the smelters as cheaply as possible and to do this the fewer the outsiders involved in the process the better so the mines had to be self-contained units as much as possible. Naturally there were a lot of items which had to he purchased from outside sources, for example, powder for blasting, oil for lamps, grease for wheels, ropes and reins for the horses but other items could be made at the mine or obtained from materials available nearby. This is where the craftsman came into his own and the two most needed were the blacksmith and the carpenter.

The carpenter's job involved making and repairing carts, wagons and hutches and making wooden wheels. The iron wheels for the hutches had to be sent from England. He also made the frames for the air doors for the air courses within the mine, wheelbarrows, repairing gantries at the mine entrance and carrying out repairs to the miner's houses. He often had to make pick and shovel handles to replace tools the miners had broken.

The blacksmith's main job was the shoeing of mine horses and repairing and sharpening tools. He helped the carpenter to make cart wheels by putting the iron hoops on them and the ironwork on the hutches and kept the wheels and hinges greased. Other work included mending and hanging gates, fixing locks etc. The smith often worked late into the night repairing wagons and wheels by candlelight in readiness for the next day's work at the mine.

14 Wellington Street, Ballymena.

Another craftsman whose services were regularly called on was the saddler. He was not employed at the mine or by the mine owner, however, but had a shop in Ballymena where he mended harnesses, back straps and reins as well as facing collars and making horse covers for the horses to wear in the mine. Horses were used for various jobs at the mine both inside and outside. They were used to haul hutches to the surface where the ore was tipped into the waiting wagons for cartage by horses to the coast. Although the railway had arrived by 1875 carting to Red Ray still continued until as late as 1911 and horses were being used for other duties away from the mine. These included the haulage of wood for mine timbers from the plantations at Glenravel House, Cleggan Lodge and Parkmore and loads of lime and sand from Red Ray pier for repairing miner's houses. Loads of peats also had to be taken from the turf banks and stacked near the mine office for use there and in the forge. The horses were mostly housed in a stable near the mine and were fed on a diet of hay, bran, oats, flax seed, India meal and potatoes so they would have been fairly fit and strong. At some of the mines the horses were kept underground after work had finished for the day and were only let out at the weekend. Needless to say when they saw daylight and smelt the fresh air they broke away from their drivers and kicked their way to a short spell of freedom. Other workers employed at the mine were the drivers and brakemen on the ore wagons and labourers, platelayers and stonebreakers on the tramway to keep it in order. Stone masons and slaters were employed for the repair and upkeep of miner's houses and mine buildings.

It will be seen, therefore, that the mine owners did everything that could be done to avoid having to depend on outside labour by including on their payroll the type of men and skills they were likely to need. There were times, however, when the working of the mines was disrupted by outside influences over which the miners had no control. An example was during the winter months, mainly February and March of 1888 when the output from the mines was drastically affected by heavy snowfalls and the miners had to dig their way into the mines. They actually spent half their working days clearing snow from the entrance adits and along the tramway. In one instance in March 1888 no ore was taken from the Crommelin Mine for six days because of heavy snow which completely covered the tramway, thus preventing the ore being taken away. (Even today, during the winter months, the Parkmore - Slievenanee area attracts heavy snowfalls while the low ground all around remains snow-free). Normally train loads of ore were being sent to Belfast and Larne daily and this inability to send any for a week prompted John Fisher to write to Captain O'Raw 'wondering if the snow was interfering with operations on the tramway and hoping the new boring machine was being used fully to reduce the cost of producing iron'. This boring machine probably referred to the improved type of rock-drill or rickety for boring shot holes in hard rock. This is the most likely explanation since in modern mining a boring machine refers to a massive mechanical drill for removing the ore face or driving tunnels and this type of machine was never used at Glenravel.

However, the question of reducing the cost of producing iron cropped up time and again and makes one wonder to what lengths the mining companies went to save money. In some cases small tonnages of bad ore were mixed with large tonnages of good ore at the tiphead and in 1888 the carrying capacity of the ore wagons was increased by heightening their sides thus reducing the cost of transportation. To cap it all Fisher wrote to Captain Hugh O'Raw, the mine manager, on 1st March 1888 as follows:

"Please see that train wagons are well loaded so that you can get a good quantity down each day – with this fine weather good work should be done. We wrote you y'day (sic) that it was better to reduce the miners' wages considerably than to send them away & no doubt you are doing this. Better stock what ore you are getting out as near the tramway as possible so that the filling won't cost much." (see letter page 50).

Again on 3rd March 1888 he wrote,
"We note what you say about Mountcashel and hope the miners will take more kindly to a reduction in wages than a total stop, We don't want them to stop if we can keep them going which we think we can do if we can manage to get the ore a little cheaper. What kind of ore is the Antrim Co. sending, is it as good, better or worse than ours"?

And on 5th March 1888,
"We shall be glad if the miners continue on at the reduced pay, but you will quite see that is as much benefit to them as to us as we have now a good deal of ore in stock." [1]

Up to this time there had been no permanent blacksmith at the Glenravel Mine and in a letter on this aspect Fisher wrote:
"Taking the lost time of man and horse shoeing and the other work done by blacksmiths at a distance from the mine we are under the impression that it would be cheaper to have a man on the spot. For how much can you get one? The loss of time taking horses away to be shod, perhaps in the middle of the day's work, must some times have a bad effect on the quantity of ore delivered at the tramend."

Fisher had several labourers working for him on his Cleggan estate and although he travelled back and forth to England the work still had to carry on. During the turf cutting season they were employed cutting and stacking peats for use at Cleggan and at the mine office although peats were also purchased from other local individuals. Sheep dipping time must have been one of celebration as the Cleggan accounts for August 1887 show:

"1 gallon whiskey 18/-, 1 pint whiskey 2/3, 1 doz. ale 2/6, 3 doz. porter 6/-, 2 doz. lemonade 1/-, in respect of drink for sheep dipping." [2]

Many miners lived a long distance from their place of work and, modes of transport not being what they are today, absenteeism and lateness were common occurrences. This prompted the mining companies to provide accommodation for their employees and in 1875 John Fisher built 14 houses at Cargan for this purpose, named Fisher's Row. The school, built in the same year, bore the name Fisherstown School up to recent years. Most of the houses still remain. A miner's row was also built at Rathkenny which is still occupied, and at Parkmore the Antrim Iron Ore Co. built 16 houses which were sold in 1934 for £15 and have since been demolished.

The following interesting entries from the wages records may be examples of persistent absenteeism:
Fortnight ending 17.2.85
Charles McMullan - filling ore at tramend one day this fortnight. (first day for him this winter) 2/-
Fortnight ending 3.3.85
20th Feb. (Friday)
Charles McMullan - 2nd day this winter 2/-

He next appears fortnight ending 26.5.85
'employed cutting peats at Parkmore' 6/5. (i.e. 6 shillings and 5 pence).

This may suggest that McMullan was reduced to labouring work because his attendance at the mines was so poor or that the miners in general were often called on to do other work away from the mines.

Another man who came to the attention of the mine owner was Charles O'Neill (Long) who had formerly been a miner but by February 1888 was employed as a platelayer on the tramway. In his letter to Captain O'Raw dated March 7th 1888 John Fisher asked:
"Kindly say how Chas O'Neill has earned his 15/- (15 shillings). What does he do?"

Having received O'Raw's prompt reply, (obviously the post in those days was speedier than it is today), Fisher wrote back on March 10th:
"We note remarks about Char's O'Neill & know he's not able for severe work. We hope he does as much as he is able for his pay."

Again, he states: *"You had better make as good a bargain as you can with John Cushenan & get him to work."* Perhaps this was a case of Cushenan having downed tools for more pay.

As mine manager it was Captain O'Raw's responsibility to ensure that a steady supply of ore was produced each week for shipment at Larne (aluminous) or Belfast (iron ore) and to achieve this by "continuing to send a daily train away" from Parkmore. "Don't miss a wagon-train that you can help." It was a rare event when this was not possible – on some days it was possible to send two trains – but on March 6th, 1888 the railway company had lent ore wagons to the Mountcashel Iron Ore Co. and there were none available for Fisher's ore so this ore had to be tipped at the 'train depot'. Understandably, this had caused some expense to Fisher as vessels were waiting in Belfast for ore cargo and couldn't leave. It was O'Raw's job to 'rouse up the Railway for causing this expense to us'. Where a shipment of ore was a matter of urgency it was necessary to send a telegram to alert Captain O'Raw to the fact.

In an earlier letter to O'Raw, Fisher had been asking him to chase up Alex Fife for rent money due to Mr Hodges but said if he (O'Raw) was not well enough then not to bother. A month later, March 13th, he enquired if he was well again but three weeks later Captain O'Raw was dead. This was a sad loss to the Fisher company and to the miners who held him in high esteem. He had been with the company since its inception and was so well thought of by the Fisher family that in 1870 he was presented with a silver pocket watch and chain by Mr Joseph Fisher, a son of the founder of the company.

As well as the rows of houses built for the miners at Cargan and Parkmore most of the small stone mountain houses in the area were built by the mining companies and rented out to the miners. Rents were paid twice a year, May and November, and went from 9 pence to 2/6 per week. There were the occasional defaulters and their rents were usually deducted from their wages. Most of these old mountain houses are now crumbling ruins, used today by sheep for shelter, but along with other old buildings still standing they help to shed some light on the mining industry and its extent. (It is known that at least one of these houses, on the Ballynahavla Road, had iron rails for its foundations). The ruins of a smithy at the Bleagh Mines are a reminder that the blacksmith was an important craftsman in those days and his skills much sought after. The ruins of another smithy can be seen at Parkmore beside the 'Tin-House Brae' (the Skerry East Road) and it is known that a blacksmith was employed at the Crommelin and Ballynahavla Mines. The ruins of explosives magazines can be seen at Bleagh, Parkmore, Slievenanee and Glenariff but like all old buildings the ravages of weather and a hundred years disuse have reduced them to rubble and made them impossible to identify by sight alone. Other larger and more robust structures remain to give credence to events though they too have suffered. Among these are the engine houses (Tuftarney), the windlasses, disused railway bridges and stations such as Cargan and Retreat, and most of all, the miner's cottages. Those at Cargan, Rathkenny and the Terrace at Red Bay are today modern dwelling houses while those at Parkmore have been demolished in the recent past as have the large two-storied ones which once stood where Benvore Park is today. Outwardly the houses haven't changed much from the early days of this century when a man was paid 30 shillings for whitewashing a whole row. By this time, of course, wages had not improved greatly from the earlier years for wage increases were not an annual event like they are today, for example, over a five week period in 1905 one particular miner, Sam McSevenney, raised 26 tons of ore from the Parkmore Mine for a wage of 2/- per ton. For the same period a workmate, Robert Steede, earned £1.4.0 and at that time there were 51 men and 6 boys employed in and around the mine. For driving a level a man could earn between £7.10.0 and £10 depending on how long or deep it was and the job would take him many weeks.

It is not surprising to learn, therefore, that even in those days men downed tools for more money. Captain Dryburgh, the engineer and Mining Captain for the Crommelin Mining Company, wrote that all the Antrim Iron Ore Co. and Crommelin Mining Co. miners were out on strike in May 1919 for better wages. About 170 miners were involved who had been in receipt of 40 shillings for a 30 hour week. They were looking for an extra 12 shillings but the Antrim Iron Ore Company offered to pay them if they worked two hours a day extra. Understandably they declined and there were ugly scenes at Parkmore. The miners blocked the railway at Parkmore with large stones and threats were made to dynamire it. This necessitated the deployment of a large force of armed police to patrol the line and keep order.[3] A month later the British Aluminium Co. wrote that there was a strike at all the mines in the Glenravel area for a number of weeks which brought the whole industry to a standstill. The company, however, was of the opinion that the strike was organised more for political reasons than in the interests of the miner's pockets.

Mining then, even as today, was often a hit and miss affair. This is evidenced by the fact that some mines were in operation for only a few years. This appears to have been the case with the Trostan Mines which were opened in 1872 and abandoned in 1874.

Silas Evans, the secretary for the Antrim *Iron Ore Co., wrote: "bear in mind the nature of this mountainous district, the distance from the sea-board, the large expenditure which will be necessary in order to erect dwelling houses for the people and in making roads, tramways and railways, and the uncertainty which attends mining enterprises, some of the most promising iron ore mines being often abandoned as worthless after trial".* [4]

Desperate measures were often called for to prolong mining such as driving costly drainage levels and lengthy boring through volcanic dykes but like all extractive industries the end must eventually come. By 1907, with the end probably in sight, the Fisher company ceased shipping their ore in their own ships from Red Bay pier to save money, opting to move all their ore by rail to Ballymena and thence to Larne or Belfast. This caused severe financial loss to the residents and farmers around Waterfoot who had been involved in work at the pier and in carting ore during their lean farming season.[5]

Three of the vessels with local connections owned by the Fisher Company were the 'Claggan', 'Fisherstown' and the 'Glenravil Miner'. The Claggan was a two-masted schooner, built by Gough & Co. at Bridgewater in 1876 and sold in 1912. The Fisherstown was a steam tug acquired much later in 1948 and sold, then broken up, in 1968. The Glenravil Miner was a two-masted schooner of 78 tons, built in 1872 by the Irvine Shipbuilding Co. She went aground and broke up on 22/9/1894.[6]

Today the mines, their outbuildings and rail sidings are derelict but no one is really to blame. Even had things gone on longer and better the result in the end would have been the same. It is a natural progression. It took Nature millions of years to produce the minerals that man needs and what the miners removed in a few short decades cannot be replaced.

In all about five million tons of good quality iron ore were removed during the period that mining flourished and although this is a long way short of the 185million tons available the remainder is regarded as uneconomical to work even though a substantial proportion of it must be good quality.

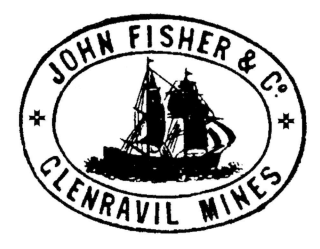

Official logo for John Fisher's mining company

Silver pocket watch given to Hugh O'Raw by Joseph Fisher

During World War Two almost 300,000 tons of bauxite were mined and considerable reserves of this still remain but with a high percentage of iron. To date, this too has been found to be uneconomical to work and the mines and the ore they contain lie abandoned, worthless, ignored and virtually forgotten.

Sources:
1. Fisher correspondence, Author's collection.
2. Cleggan account 1887, Author's collection.
3. The Irish News, May 17, 1919.
4. Correspondence, Author's collection.
5. Northern Whig, Dec 5, 1907.
6. Around the Coast & Across the Seas, Nigel Watson. St. Matthew's Press, 2000

Fisher's Buildings,
Barrow-in-Furness,
March 1st 1888

Enclosures.

Captain O'Raw
Glenravil Mines
Nr Ballymena.

Dear Sir,
we have received your letter & note contents. The weight question now seems to be in order. We hope you have got what one Captain Iddon requires to Belfast & that you are sending on the Aluminous to Larne — Please see that tram wagons are well loaded so that you can get a good quantity down each day — With this fine weather good work should be done. We wrote you yday that it was better to reduce the miners wages considerably than to send them away — no doubt you are doing this. Better stock what ore you are getting out as near the tram way as possible so that the filling wont cost much. —

Yours faithfully
JAMES FISHER & SONS.
James Fisher.

Letter from James Fisher & Sons to Captain O'Raw

Chapter Five
Mining Methods

A gantry

Iron is recorded as having been worked as far back as 5,000 years ago by various Middle Eastern cultures. Some regarded it as a precious metal to be used only for ornaments or to adorn burial chambers or for ceremonial occasions. In this context it has been found in the tombs of ancient Egypt in small amounts and in Homer's Iliad a lump of iron was offered as a prize in the games. Throughout the ages iron objects, tools and weapons have been used and iron technology and improvements in the smelting process developed but it wasn't until 1856 when the Bessemer process was introduced that the demand for iron increased to manufacture all sorts of iron and steel products. Today it is so common that no one goes through the day without touching something made from iron. This illustrates its status as the most useful metal ever to have been discovered and indeed it is the second most abundant metal in the Earth's crust. Iron and steel are the lifeblood and framework of our civilisation and the possession of iron ore reserves, along with coal for smelting it, determines the industrial strength of a nation.

Although Co. Antrim had considerable reserves of iron ore she did not have good quality coal or the facilities for smelting it so the ore had to be shipped mainly to North West England where the big blast furnaces were located. As well as this the mining companies were invariably English-based with the result that the wealth gained from Antrim's ore deposits went across the water, apart from the wages paid to the miners. The miners had only to extract the ore and send it on its way, and how they did just that is of most interest to us.

Normally before mine production can commence the venture must pass through several distinct phases extending over a number of years. Initially, a geological survey would be carried out to prove the existence of the deposits and evaluate their extent. This involves drilling boreholes to define the shape and size of the ore body and determine the grade of the ore. Only following this would mining commence. Fisher's methods may have been a little less involved and perhaps there was some element of luck attached to his endeavours but he was none the less successful. He already knew the grade of the ore from Professor Hodges' analysis and of previous scattered finds denoting a wide-ranging deposit. The ore outcropped on the surface at several places so he knew where to start operations and he was wise enough to begin by opencast mining thus enabling him to ascertain the dip of the ore seam. All he had to do then was to follow it. Other companies may not have had it so easy in opening non-adjoining tracts and in the Crommelin tract at least boreholes were sunk.

At the commencement of mining operations a level was driven at the lowest point of the outcrop consistent with facilities for loading ore wagons. A parallel level was driven and connected to the first to provide a circulation of air to the miners, to disperse explosives fumes and prevent the build-up of foul air such as Carbon Monoxide. As soon as a sound roof was met with and the quality of ore good enough to work side roads were driven right and left and from these the working areas branched off approximately eight yards apart. In these areas the miner excavated the ore with pick and shovel in a cramped and awkward position lying on his side.

Discarded shovel,
Salmon's Drift

From this stage the mine was extended by merely following the ore seam. The ore occurred in bedded masses or seams and where the roof was sound, as was generally the case, was mined on the 'longwall' principle in which the ore was removed over wide areas and timbering and waste rock used to support the roof. If the roof was found to be unstable pillars of rock were left standing to support it giving rise to the term 'pillar and stall' method. Examples of both methods can be found in many of the Glenravel mines. Connecting passages would continue to be driven and in a few cases air shafts were sunk to improve ventilation and air flow, e.g. Parkmore Mine. In modern mining the workings are ventilated by huge extractor fans used in conjunction with ventilation shafts. This is understandable when it is realised that most modern mines are deep mines. The iron ore mines on the other hand were drift mines, i.e. they were worked on a horizontal plane.

Probably early in the process rails were laid into the mine to provide a means of removing waste rock as well as ore. For this reason the main adit was driven 7ft high by 8ft wide to allow a double line of rails to be laid. Alternatively, if the level was for ventilation only, i.e. an air drift, or a single line was considered sufficient the level was driven only 5ft wide. As the workings progressed the waste rock or pavement cuttings, along with 'brushings' and other rubbish would be used to support the roof behind the miner as he moved forward or, at a later stage, to block off workings which became exhausted.

Blocked side road, Salmon's Drift

In driving the levels and extracting the ore there were various jobs. Solid rock had to be blasted loose and this involved the drilling of shot holes. For this job a long iron drill known as a jumper was used. This was about 4ft long with a thick solid end and a long thin shaft with a broad chisel-like point. To use it was a two-man operation; one held the jumper and the other struck it with a hammer into the rock in a slightly downward motion, then as a hole developed the jumper was rotated through 90 degrees and hammered in again. During the drilling the hole filled with rock chips and dust and had to be cleared out with a scraper, a thin metal, hooked rod which hoked out the offending grit. The process was repeated until a hole was drilled deep enough to take explosives. Usually three holes were driven and charged. The centre hole was blown first and then the two outer holes which removed the rock towards the centre. A miner by the name of Rab McNeill had his face burnt and blackened in a mine near Ballynahavla Bridge (Ballynahavla Pit). A charge he had planted didn't fire and the fact wasn't reported to the mine captain. McNeill went back to the face and drove his pick into the rock. The charge blew up in his face and he survived the explosion but he carried the black marks with him for the rest of his life.

In later years the type of drill was improved and consisted of a ratchet device which could be jammed against a solid wall or timber prop and turned to provide the drilling action. This device was known as a rickety, probably from the sound it made, and could be used for boring very hard rock. It may well have been the item referred to as a 'boring machine' in letters between John Fisher and the mine manager Captain O'Raw in March 1888. It was used for drilling upwards into the rock and required water for lubrication and for clearing out the holes. Smooth, clean shot holes found at roof level in the Rathkenny Mine were probably made by such a drill. However, the old faithful jumper continued in use even in the mines worked during the last war.

In the early years of mining blasting was done with powder and cord. It was only in 1874 that dynamite came into regular use for mining operations in England and was adapted in Ireland some years later as the wages books for the Glenravel Mines show that powder was still being used at least up to 1888. However, there can be no doubt that dynamite was eventually used. One stick was found still in its wrapping paper in one particular mine. During World War II dynamite was used exclusively in the mines for blasting. Dynamite has a disruptive force about eight times that of gunpowder and naturally requires careful handling. Its use therefore was generally entrusted to one man who knew how to work with it. He usually went round the mine with his box of explosives and detonators and did his blasting wherever required. However, it appears from reliable information that if he knew the miner at any particular spot was capable of using dynamite he left a few sticks and caps with him and proceeded on his way. No doubt if his employers had known of this he would have been in deep trouble.

The method employed was slightly different from that used with powder blasting. Firstly the layer of clayey rock known as 'brushings', only a few inches thick and situated between the ore seam and the roof, was stripped off by scraping it out to form a bench. Shot holes were then drilled – two would suffice – in the centre of the bench face and when the charges were fired the face was removed in a mass of rubble. The process could then be repeated if necessary.

As the rock and ore were removed another miner, the timberman, was responsible for inserting roof supports where this was deemed necessary with suitably trimmed tree trunks and wedges or blocks, known as trees and lids, to ensure a tight fit. Occasionally the basalt roof bulged downwards, not because it was weaker at that point but merely because the lava which formed it was poured out on an uneven landscape. The miners referred to this bulge as a pot-ass perhaps from its similarity to the bottom of a three-legged iron cooking pot. It was regarded as a danger point because of the possibility of collapse and therefore required support. It was here that trees and lids were mostly used and many's a miner, while having a rest, could hear the timbers creak and break and see the water being squeezed out of the freshly cut wood as the roof strove to fill up the empty space created by the miner. The latter spent most of his time in the low side workings where he worked out the ore over a wide expanse using the longwall system. As he worked he piled the waste rock behind him in place of the ore he had just removed and occasionally inserted short timbers known as dollies.

The ore was removed by the fathom, that is, a fathom forward and between two and ten feet in height. The usual rate of excavation was about three fathoms by five feet but if the seam was thicker the forward progress would be less and vice versa. Extraction was mainly with pick and shovel and often in cramped and awkward conditions and even today the marks of pick and shovel can still be plainly seen in all of the mines, bearing excellent witness to the skill, craftsmanship and sheer hard work of the early miners. The average thickness of the No.1 or pisolitic ore was about 14 inches and beneath this lay the No.2 ore or ferruginous bauxite averaging five feet in thickness. An ore seam of 12 to 16 inches could suddenly thicken to 25 or 30 inches due to a rise in the roof, a roll or gurry as the miners called it. Alternatively, an undulating roof might cause the seam to thin and thicken in parallel to the roof. Below the No.2 ore lay the pavement, so called because it forms the floor of the iron ores. It is in this the levels were driven and was soft enough to be cut with the pick. Below this was the lithomarge, violet in colour with white mottled spots, which in turn rested on the Lower Basalt.

Where the good ore was compact or solid the miner undercut it about a fathom forward and then brought it down by blasting or by using wedges. This type of ore was known as shooting ore whereas that which could be removed by the pick was called hoking ore. At 20 to 30 fathoms from the outcrop the ore was usually too hard for pick working and was also harder as the thickness of the roof or perpendicular height increased. In Fisher's mines the best seams of ore yielded 60% iron and the average yield was about one ton of ore per cubic yard. At Evishacrow the quality was also good and the peas of iron (hence the name pisolitic) in the ore had the appearance 'when split of cast steel'. At Cargan the ore was up to 40% iron falling to 18% in the poorer seams.

In some mines the pisolitic ore was replaced by aluminous clay or bauxite situated in the same position beneath the Upper Basalt. In the pisolitic bed the peas of iron were found to diminish in size and number gradually merging into the bauxitic clay. The bauxite, after drying, yielded 33 to 60% aluminium. At the other end of the seam the bauxite merged gradually back to pisolitic iron ore.

Associated with the ores of iron and aluminium were occasionally found seams of lignite probably formed from the vegetation which flourished during the Interbasaltic Period. In places e.g. Ballintoy, this was in sufficient quantity to be mined but in the Mid-Antrim area the only mine in which it can still be seen is at Rathkenny where it attains a thickness of between two and three feet and where pieces of carbonised wood and tree bark can be picked from the walls of the mine. Where lignite was encountered it always overlay the bauxite. In 'The Geology of Ireland' Prof. Charlesworth mentions that sometimes the lignite in the mines caught fire and smouldered for several years but this must have referred to the Ballintoy Mines.

Seepage of water from the roof made the miner's lot very uncomfortable and in such places he wore a cape of glazed cloth over his shoulders to let the water run off. Working underground the miner required light and this was provided by the sweet oil lamp which he hooked on his cap. It gave a very poor intensity of light, no better than a candle, for it only provided a bare, smoky flame with no reflector. It was only much later - during World War II - that carbide lamps were used in the mines.

From left: A miner's sweet oil lamp (the mine Captian would have had a bigger lamp), a miner's pick and oil flask

After digging out the ore it was loaded into hutches, the four-wheeled wagons or bogies which carried ore from the work face. These were mounted on rails running into each side road and adjacent to each work face and from here the ore was conveyed to the main road and thence to the surface. The miners were paid 'by the hutch' and a hutch-keeper or tallyman was employed to keep count of the number of hutches going to the surface. In the early years of mining the hutches held about eight hundredweight of ore each but later on this capacity was increased to 13½ and then to 14 hundredweight. The miners received about 10 pence to 1 shilling per hutch of good ore but less for bad ore and it is firmly believed that they regularly deceived the tallyman by mixing the bad with the good and getting paid the higher rate and that this practice led to the ore being considered unsuitable for the smelters and thus hastened the closure of the mines. For aluminous ore or bauxite they were paid three pence per hutch and a hard working miner could fill as many as five hutches in a day or 'get, fill and trail a distance of about 50 yards, in a shift of eight hours, from two to four tons of ore according to the thickness and character of the seam'.

As the ore was removed and the mine extended the daily advance of each miner was measured by the mine manager, or Captain as he was called, and recorded in the Miner's Underground book at the end of each fortnightly pay. Both forward advance and height of working were shown, the first in fathoms and the latter in feet and inches, e.g.-

Miner's Fortnight ending 4th August 1886
Dan'l McAteer and Mick McCarthy   *1 fath. 4½ ft. high,*
    1 fath. 2½ ft. also 3 faths. 2½ ft. deep.
John McAteer   *3 faths. 2 ½ feet high for air.*
Chas O'Neill and son   *3 faths. & 2 feet, 4'/6 4'/9 5'/0.*

This daily advance was also used as the basis for drawing up the plans of the mines.

Within the mines the various and extensive networks of galleries were divided into two main groups, as is the case today in modern mining. There were passages to the mineral-producing workings and passages for services. The passages to the workings were known as side roads and were accessible from the surface by means of the service passages known as main roads. In some mines the latter were further subdivided into horse roads or horse drifts. There were also air drifts for ventilation purposes but these were the exception rather than the rule. (The term drift means a horizontal adit from the surface and is derived from the verb 'to drive' as in – to drive a level). The differences in the various types of roadway becomes more apparent when the mine itself becomes a maze of passages.

The main difference lies in their construction. Roads to mineral workings were used frequently while the ore was being excavated and since the miners were spending a considerable amount of time in them it was necessary to use more roof support to prevent collapse and possible entombment. However, when the workings became exhausted the side road would be used infrequently or not at all and eventually would be blocked off altogether. On the other hand the main roads or service ways would remain in use until the mine itself was abandoned. For this reason more care was taken in their construction. They were always straighter, higher and more square in shape with sound walls most of the way to the roof. With the roof thus supported there was little need for timbering and very few roof timbers were used.

Occasionally the roads were driven through dykes, hard intrusions of volcanic rock like the North Star Dyke on the seashore at Ballycastle. Sometimes these were only a few yards thick, others 20, 50 or a hundred or more feet. The roads through them were sometimes arched at the top thus making them extremely safe and sound and requiring no other form of support. Others produced sharp, angular edges of the black rock sometimes cracked and prone to collapse as in the Dyke Level of Salmon's Drift. Normally the roads were high enough to walk upright in with occasional holes driven into the roof to locate the ore seam. Since the dykes merely displaced the ore seam upwards the miners knew it was there but had no idea how far it had been displaced. In general they were fortunate and the seam was found after only a matter of feet and worked at this level, thus giving rise to workings above the main roadways. This can be seen in many instances, notably at Cargan, Parkmore, Evishacrow and Rathkenny. In other cases the seam was not found and the holes in the roof developed into shafts going up 20 or 30 feet to dead ends, e.g. Glenravel Mine and Rathkenny.

The blocking off of side roads with waste rock or deads served a useful purpose in diverting air to other workings and passages. An airtight seal was obtained by applying wet mud over and between the deads. This was known as plastering and in it can still be seen the hand and fingerprints of the miners who performed this mucky task. Diverting air for ventilation was also achieved by the construction of air doors and the remains of many of these can be seen to this day. They consisted merely of two uprights and one horizontal beam across which wet sacks or other heavy material could be nailed thus preventing the flow of air from passing that way. The movement of hutches into and out of the mine and through the air doors also helped with the circulation of air.

From the side roads, therefore, the hutches of ore were pushed to the main road and thence to the surface. Ponies were sometimes used for this purpose, hence the horse roads referred to. Several of the hutches were coupled together to form a small train and hauled out. A story goes that one of these trains was being hauled to the surface at the Parkmore Mine. As the mines were driven horizontally the surface was not necessarily uphill; in this case there was a slight downhill gradient for the sole purpose of draining the mine under gravity. A man was employed on this gradient to brake the last hutch by pushing an iron bar or snibble through the rear wheels. This had the effect of jamming the wheels so that they slid along the rails and prevented the hutches from gathering speed. On this occasion the man involved, John Birt from Cargan, missed the wheels with the bar and before he could do anything about it the hutches were gathering speed and eventually caught up with and overran the unfortunate horse, causing its demise. Its bones lie buried outside the entrance to the mine.

Rails, 2½ feet gauge, were laid in all the main roads and most of the side roads and in some places where the road was narrow grooves have been worn in the walls where the wheel hubs and top edges of the hutches have rubbed on countless journeys. Some mines had passing places where two lines of rails allowed hutches to pass, e.g. at Rathkenny and Parkmore. The imprints of rails and sleepers still remain in every mine to show the layout of the rail system since they themselves have long since been removed. A few discarded curved rails still remain propped against walls or spanning roadways to support the roof. In the Parkmore Mine and Salmon's Drift short sections of rail remain in place in upper levels and in Glentask Mine, Bushmills many L-shaped rails have been lifted and discarded at the side of the roadways. It was sometimes necessary to lift rails and sleepers from disused side roads and relay them in new workings. This was just another job for the hard-worked miner and was probably just as strenuous and back-breaking as mining the ore.

In the early years of mining there was no mineral railway to transport the ore for shipment and roads were only muddy tracks. Horse-drawn transport was used and the ore taken to Red Bay pier. The situation was improved somewhat with the construction of the Wire Tramway but unfortunately this only lasted a short time. Then with the coming of the railway through the area offshoots were laid to the various mining tracts between Rathkenny and Parkmore. The mineral railways joined the main line at Martinstown, Cargan, Evishacrow and Parkmore. At Rathkenny a short, straight siding was all that was required. There was an older mineral railway which served the old Trostan Mines but these were by this time disused and the line derelict. As will be explained later, this was in fact a horse tramway and had no connection with the new rail system although both can still be seen where they almost meet at the head of Gault's Road in Ballyeamon.

When the hutches, therefore, arrived at the surface they were run out to the side of the mineral railway for loading into the hoppers. This was done by manually shovelling the ore into the wagons but at some mines, e.g. Evishacrow and Parkmore, a wooden gantry was required as the railway lay several feet below the mine mouth. Here the ore was tipped from the hutches into the enclosed base of the gantry and from there via chutes to the hoppers alongside (see below). At least one mine at Tuftarney had a stone-built loading-bay with chutes for loading the ore. With the railway now serving the mines the ore was transported by train to Belfast and Larne and thence to North West England for smelting. The carters were still employed to cart ore to Red Bay as well so that there was an almost continual traffic of ore from the mines. Even so, it was necessary at times to stockpile ore at the tramend, i.e. the end of the mineral railway nearest the mine, to await transport. For example, in 1886 the output of ore from the Glenravel Mine at Ballynahavla was 10161 tons. On top of this there were 9085 tons stockpiled at 1.1.86 and of this total only 9307 tons were sent away by train during that year. This left a total of 9939 tons in stock at 1.1.87 as well as 9000 tons of aluminous ore. This aluminous ore or bauxite was always taken to the British Aluminium Company at Larne, founded in 1895, from whence it was sent to their processing plant at Foyers in Scotland. The only other exception to the general run of things was at the Bleagh or Mountcashel Mines. Here can be seen the remains of the wash-house, crusher and settling ponds where the mined ore was washed and dressed before being taken away by train. The leat which carried the water for these operations also remains. This procedure was not carried out at any of the other mines, but this could be due to the fact that the Mountcashel Company did not work any other mines in the area and it was simply their particular policy to do this.

This process of washing and crushing the ore was intended to raise the metallic content of the mined ore by freeing the nodules of iron from the poorer matrix, the object being to put the ore on the market solely for its iron content, thus making it more valuable, and not simply for use as a flux for which it had previously been used. The Mountcashel Company represented the Ebbw Vale Iron and Steel Company of South Wales whose requirements in 1874 were 2,000 tons of ore per week. However, while some believed that the extra yield obtained did not justify the additional cost involved others were of the opinion that the best quality ore was being washed away and indeed it is thought that this ore still lies at the bottom of the settling ponds beside the ruined wash-house. As well as this the mining company was plagued by severe flooding problems and only managed to prolong mining for a few years by costly tunnelling to provide drainage.

At times the miners would be required to do surface work. It was possible for a miner to spend half a day in the mine doing the various jobs connected with raising the ore including timbering and clearing water courses and the other half on the surface loading it on the wagons or working on the tramway. Often they had their sons helping them, boys in their early teens, but only one wage was paid based on the amount of work done or fathoms driven. Some miners even worked at night as well as their daily shift but it appears from wages records that this was an exception rather than a rule. The normal shift in the Glenravel and other mines of the 19th century was 7am to 3pm. but the conditions were vastly different to Lyle's Hill and other bauxite mines

Author in Lyle's Hill Mine

worked during the last war. This was because in the bauxite mines the roads and workings were much higher and wider and carbide lamps were much superior to the old oil lamps. Very few of the bauxite mines extended as far below ground as the iron mines so the latter day miners had not so far to travel to the workface and could do so without having to crouch or creep.

Sources:
Information from Author's father who worked in the Templepatrick Mines.
Royal Geological Society of Ireland Journal, Vol XV1, 1882-84.
The Iron Mines of Antrim, R A Watson, Dublin University Magazine Vol 83, 1874.
Practical Notes on the Mining of Iron Ores & Bauxites of Co. Antrim, C H Williams, Manchester Geological Society transactions, 1894.

Author's Note: My grandfather who worked in the Bleagh Mines finished his shift at 3pm. and came down from the mines on one of the railway wagons and jumped off near his home, a short distance away. The other miners continued on to Martinstown.

Chapter Six
The Mining Tracts

Ballynahavla Pit (James Fisher Jr in foreground).
Photo courtesy of James Fisher & Sons Archives

Fisher's Tramway

Salmon's Drift Dyke Level

The objects for which the Company is established are :—

(1.) To acquire, either directly or otherwise, from Mr. Frederick Armand de la Chirois Crommelin, or some other person or persons, and to adopt or hold a lease or leases of certain mines, minerals and mining rights, situate in the Townland of Newtown Crommelin, in the County of Antrim, in the Province of Ulster, Ireland.

(2.) To prove, develope and extend the said mines and minerals.

(3.) To purchase, take on lease or on license, or otherwise acquire any land, buildings, iron or other mines, minerals, machinery, plant, vessels, rolling stock, waterworks, gasworks, ponds, reservoirs, water courses, railways, tramways, wharves, piers, docks, canals and other buildings and works, easements, licenses, patents, patent-rights and privileges calculated to be or to become profitable to the Company.

(4.) To carry on the trades or business of iron ore pro-prietors, miners, and mining engineers, in all their respective branches.

Crommelin Mining Company Ltd details of directors and Memorandum and Articles of Association

Heard's Drift

North Antrim in shape resembles a large but shallow saucer, the coast itself being part of its rim. Because of this saucer-like shape all the beds of rock tilt in towards the centre. This can be seen to be true if one travels by car from north to south or east to west. From Ballymena the road rises to the Antrim plateau, to Fair Head in the north, Cave Hill in the south, Garron Point to the east and Long Mountain to the west. This saucer-like shape was a contributing factor in the search for minerals because the ore in the Interbasaltic Layer rose towards the rim. The miners found that when they reached the extremity of a slope it was financially unprofitable to start digging downwards and so mining ceased. In some mines this slope is barely noticeable while in others e.g. Parkmore and Evishacrow, it is quite evident. This incline from the mine mouth enabled water to drain out of the mine under gravity thus obviating the need for pumps.

However, some mines had to be abandoned because of the unfavourable dip of the ore seam which often caused flooding and necessitated the driving of expensive tunnels for drainage purposes. In other cases the seam got thinner as the miners progressed and the working became unprofitable.

In short, therefore, most profitable mines were driven on south-facing slopes while those driven on north-facing slopes didn't last long or had drainage problems e.g. Glenariff Mines and Mountcashel Mines.

The locations of the main groups of mines have already been referred to. It only remains now to elaborate on the individual mines and their place in the iron ore industry as a whole.

THE GLENRAVEL TRACT
Situated north of Cargan village on the south-facing slope of Slievenanee, these were the first mines in the area to be opened by James Fisher in 1867 following his months of opencast mining at the Gullets. Thus they gave birth to the Antrim iron ore industry and were named after the glen in which they were situated.

The ore was removed from these mines by means of a narrow tramway, about a mile long, constructed by Fisher as far as Ballynahavla Bridge. A photograph from the archives of James Fisher and Sons, Barrow-in-Furness, shows a small steam locomotive at the Bridge around the late 1860's but this is long before the coming of the narrow gauge railway so it is doubtful if the date on the photo is correct. The locomotive is smaller than a narrow gauge engine but it is obvious from the wages records that the tramway was initially designed for horse traction and later converted for steam usage. From here the ore was taken by horse and cart to Red Ray for shipment. The path of the tramway can still be plainly followed.

Following the coming of the B.C.R.R. to Parkmore a siding was laid back to Ballynahavla Bridge where it met up with Fisher's Tramway. The old Ordnance Survey maps show the Parkmore Siding crossing the road at this point, suggesting that it joined with the tramway. It appears from the photograph that the tramway gauge was also three feet, making it compatible with the narrow gauge line. This also means that the tramway pre-dates the Glenariff Railway, which was also private, and it is regarded as the first narrow gauge line in Ireland. The construction of the siding, therefore, would have enabled the ore from Fisher's mines to be transported all the way from the mines to Parkmore Station. The mined ore was shipped to N.W. England for smelting, using Fisher's own ships from Red Bay pier, a total of 18000 tons in the first six months. The ore was good quality, the best seams yielding 60% of iron and seams varied from a few inches to an exceptionally rich deposit of 10 feet in thickness. The average yield was 1 ton of ore per cubic yard.

By 1912 many of the original adits had been abandoned and mining was being carried on at Ballynahavla Pit which runs below the road at Ballynahavla Bridge. Mining ceased on 29th October 1913 because the best quality ore had been worked out and the second quality ore was found to be unprofitable.

One of the adits to the Glenravel Mine is still accessible and leads via a devious route of flat-out crawls to workings over 15 feet in height. There is a little evidence of roof collapse in some of the side roads but the main road is sound, dead straight, high and wide but blocked at the surface and is only accessible as described above. The workings themselves cover a vast area and contain many features which demonstrate how the miners worked. The hob-nailed footprints of long-dead miners are plainly visible in the inner reaches. It is believed the mine connected with the Crommelin Mines to the west and Ballynahavla Pit and Parkmore Mine to the east but it is impossible from an underground perspective to say where one starts and the other finishes. It is one of the few dry mines in the area, only a fraction of which has been rediscovered.

THE CROMMELIN TRACT (see also chapter on The Drum)

These mines, to the west of and adjacent to the above mentioned workings, extend northwards under the western slope of Slievenanee along the valley of the Skerry Water and include the mines of Tuftarney Hill and two bauxite mines on Skerry Hill. William Crossley and George Bargate of Dalton-in-Furness who formed the Crommelin Iron Ore Co., commenced mining about 1876, having leased lands in Legagrane townland from the Antrim Iron Ore co. but the company only lasted a few years (see Chapter on The Inclined Plane). On 8/9/1888 a lease between the Crommelin Mining Co Ltd and Frederick Delacherois Crommelin (grandson of Nicholas of Newtowncrommelin), was drawn up and from that date mining continued with an extensive excavation along the east bank of the river and just a few feet below the surface which in this area is fairly level. The main mines are Herd's Drift, opened 1st April 1889, Salmon's Drift (also named Solomon's Drift), opened October 1891, Walker's Drift, opened 1st April 1902, and Spittal's Drift, opened 16th September 1911. They all mainly extend eastwards under Slievenanee and cover an area about a mile long by a quarter of a mile wide.

A mineral railway was constructed to serve these mines and connected to the main line at Cargan station via 'the Drum'. Its course is still plainly visible and can be traversed for all of its distance, making a fine afternoon's walk for the outdoor type.

The mines at Tuftarney Hill were worked from 1874 to 1891 for iron ore and to 1912 for bauxite and iron ore. From 1912 to about 1930 they were worked wholly for bauxite. They are now flooded and used as a source of water. Herd's Drift was abandoned in 1908 due to flooding but another level was driven from another direction to reach the dry workings and an air shaft sunk to ventilate them. However, by 1910 this new working had to be abandoned also due to the unfavourable dip of the roof. Spittal's Drift too was soon closed but reopened again in 1916.

Iron ore mining ceased in 1928 and the company, the Crommelin Mining Co. Ltd., turned their attention to the bauxite mines on Skerry Hill. However, a dangerous and near fatal roof fall at the mine mouth put the seal on this enterprise and work was abandoned in 1931.

Of all the mines worked by the Crommelin company in this royalty only two have been explored – Herd's Drift and Salmon's Drift. The former is now sealed but was flooded to a depth of five feet for most of its length and a huge roof-fall at one point has left only a few inches of rock between the mine and the grazing above. Woe betide the driver of any vehicle which passes over it. Salmon's Drift is now gated but has been explored for long distances to the north, south and east of the entrance adit and the plans show literally miles of workings many of which are blocked off and inaccessible. The main level contains a small active stream which eventually fills the passage to the roof at its southern extremity. Bats have been noted hibernating in this mine.

The mine has been used for countless field and film trips as it was at that time easily accessible and most of its roadways are high enough to walk upright in. About a quarter mile in it is traversed by a large volcanic dyke which displaces the ore seam upwards, the Dyke Level. Both bauxite and iron ore occur and an abundance of calcite has been deposited since mining ceased. It appears from the plans that the miners could have crossed into the Glenravel Mine to the east but a large roof fall at the end of the accessible route has effectively sealed the way through.

The Crommelin Company went into liquidation in 1934.

During World War II Salmon's Drift was re-opened for bauxite (1942) as part of the re-investigation of reserves for the war effort. It only lasted three weeks as there was no hope of profitable working owing to flooding.

EVISHACROW AND CHAMBER'S MINES

These mines, clearly visible from the main road just above Cargan, were opened by Mr. Charles Chambers of Clough about 1869 for iron ore. Further trials were made on the north side of the hill but little is known of these though a flooded adit has been found and the original plans still exist but there is no link with the other mines. The hill itself is honeycombed with workings with evidence from fox prints of a 'back door'. The mines were closed for many years (1890-1897) and then reopened by the Crommelin Mining Co. Ltd. in 1897 mainly for bauxite. The Nos. 3 and 4 adits were finally closed on 31st December 1923 because of the company's inability to work them at a profit. The British Portland Cement Manufacturing Co. then operated the bauxite mine from 1925 for the manufacture of cement at Magheramorne but this ceased on 7th August 1926 because the mineral proved unsuitable for that purpose.

These mines too were served by the ill-fated Wire Tramway and after the coming of the narrow gauge railway a short siding was built to carry the ore to the main line nearby. Mr. R. A. Watson, C.E.M.E., in his report of the mining industry in the Dublin University Magazine of January 1874 was much impressed by the quality of ore in Evishacrow stating that the nodules of iron in the ore had the appearance 'when split of cast steel'.

Two adits to the Evishacrow Mine are still open but are at different heights on the hillside and are not thought to be linked. Much of the lower mine workings have collapsed especially in the vicinity of the small quarry visible from the road but from the extent of debris within the mine it seems that dynamiting in an attempt to seal the mine was the cause. Access is still possible and beyond the first 100 feet or so the rock is sound. Mining was on two levels with most of the workings in the upper level. Many of the passages are very low and the mine also features steeply inclined roads and holes in the roof giving access to upper workings or enabling ore to be thrown down into hutches below. The upper workings are never far below the surface for most of the adits are driven on the 900ft contour and the hill is just over 1,000 feet high. Local knowledge has it that there were two air shafts to the mines, one known as the Burn Pit, but there is no trace of either. They are presumably filled in.

From the area of this mining tract it is estimated that, at one ton of ore per cubic yard, approximately six million tons of iron ore remain to be mined. With a thin basalt cap opencast mining may therefore be feasible.

PARKMORE AND ESSATHOHAN TRACTS

Shortly after Fisher's success at the Glenravel Mines the Parkmore Iron Ore Company opened up mines about a mile to the north east near the junction of the Glenariff and Ballyeamon roads. In 1880 the Antrim Iron Ore Company took over and extended the workings. Various adits were opened northwards from the railway station and nearby the company also worked iron ore and bauxite at Essathohan Drift. This mine passed into the hands of the Crommelin Mining Company Ltd. who abandoned it on 22nd June 1934 due to foreign competition. A trial mine was driven in the west face of the Essathohan Gorge which remains open (see below). It runs for about 60 yards and stops abruptly against solid rock. The writer is reliably informed that another adit on this side existed but no trace of it now remains. The Antrim Co. also carried out trials round Trostan Mountain in 1872 and 1873 but these were abandoned early in 1874 as worthless. Further working took place in the late 1890's but this too was soon to stop.

The main interest at Parkmore was centred on the mine near the now disused railway station, opposite to where the old miners' cottages, Miners' Row, were located and iron ore only was mined, there being

Salmon's Drift

Ardclinis Mine (left of waterfall)

Essathohan Trial

Cargan Mine, behind Sunray Crescent

Coffin Level

no bauxite in Parkmore. The ore mined was good quality yielding at its best 40% iron though hand picked samples had as much as 60%. Second quality ore yielded 28% iron which was better than the second quality of most other mines. Samples of magnetite have been recovered from the spoil heaps at Parkmore by the writer.

In mining the ore it was found that the further in one progressed the harder the ore became and it had to be blasted out. The seam rose at an incline of 1 in 22 to the west and the mine passage rose in steps to follow it. Although this would have enabled the mine to be drained by gravity a large section of this mine is now flooded by seepage from streams originating on the mountain above which traverse the mine and issue from the half-choked adit. The quantity of water involved would suggest that even when the mine was being worked water was a problem which may have been a factor in the reason for closure of the mine in 1923.

This extensive mine is still accessible but involves a long swim and wade through the flooded section which averages 4ft deep with five feet at the mine mouth. The main road is fairly straight and wide and has been explored by the writer and friends for well over a mile with no end in sight. It contains an abundance of calcite on floor and walls. An air shaft not far from the entrance goes up to the surface where it is marked by a sealed depression among the pine trees. These trees have now been cut down. Another air shaft, formerly hidden in thick forest about a quarter of a mile away, descends vertically for about 60 feet to a blockage of earth, branches and rubbish. These trees have also been cleared and the shaft is now marked and capped. About 400 yards north of the main adit a smaller and long-abandoned mine was reopened by the writer early in 1977, explored for a short distance and then resealed. No link with the main mine was found but this could have been due to the fact that the workings became exceptionally low at a point probably close to or below the Skerry East Road and no attempt was made to venture on. With forest clearance, another adit, next to the latter, has now become visible.

THE GLENARIFF TRACT
These mines extend from the head of the famous Glenariff Glen, in the gorge of the Inver River, down the south east side of the glen. They were opened in 1873 and lasted about nine years. The ore bed was 720 feet above sea level and inclined at 1 in 30 to the south east. This means the mines would have been liable to flooding and ideas of re-opening them in 1908 were abandoned because of this, as it would have involved tunnelling at a lower level to relieve the mines of water. There were eleven

adits on this side of the glen but a further four were driven on the west side of the Inver River where the seams were thicker and better.

Nearer the sea were the Bay Mines and further trials were carried out at Ardclinis and in the gorge of the Cushenilt Burn but the ore here was very poor and, apart from a visit by the author in April 1977 and the summer of '87 little is known of these mines. Access to them was extremely difficult as the following passage from the author's explorations demonstrate:

"By now the thin red band of the Interbasaltic Bed was clearly visible on the left hand wall of the upper gorge but there was no sign of the mine level which I had come to examine. The terraces of upper basalt rose above me like a tiered cake showing clearly the volcanic sequences which had built up these massive lava flows to form the Antrim plateau. I climbed slowly and carefully onwards, scanning the cliffs as I went, until I reached the relative security of the thick tufted grass which is a feature of the plateau summit - only a few more yards now to the boundary fence and over it to safety. I was at the apex of the gorge. A few yards along to the right I was able to make out the small one metre opening of a trial mine. There was no visible means of access to it either from the side or below. It lay about 8 metres below the cliff top and I had no plans or means to get to it by that route. I decided it was not worth closer inspection as it appeared very similar to the trial mine in the gorge of the Carrivemurphy Burn which was easier of access but of no real interest. So I abandoned the Crearlagh Mine and set off across the plateau, determined not to risk the perilous path by which I had come.

My next port of call was the mining adit at the head of the Ardclinis Gorge but this was still a long way off so I struck off inland to shorten the journey.

At the top of Ardclinis, where the two streams merge before cascading down the small waterfall, I had no difficulty in locating the mine level. Its wide mouth gaped at me from beside the base of the fall where the waters tumble into a deep pool. It was an idyllic setting and I quickly scrambled down the grassy stream bank to examine the adit more closely. I was not equipped for exploring the mine save for my electric caving lamp so I just shone the beam into the mine from a position inside the entrance. The floor was covered in crystal-clear water about half a metre deep and the roof, about 2 metres high, dipped gently towards the rear of the passage. I could see at least 20 metres of passage with a small side working going off on the left and no doubt the mine had been worked for ore though it is likely the amount extracted was small. This is only one of several adits at Ardclinis but none of the others were visible, being long since blocked up. Ignoring the cart track on the west bank, by which the ore had been transported away, after a brief rest I decided to return via the gorge itself to sea-level about a mile away and 800 feet lower down". (The Glynns, Vol 16, 1988).

Ore from the Ardclinis Mines was removed by a steep inclined plane down the face of the scarp by means of a wooden trough. It was then carted to Red Bay pier for shipping.

One of the mines on the west bank of the Inver is still open but only for a short distance. In it were found a smashed six-gallon wine jar and a fire grate, evidence that a once-famous poteen maker, who shepherded on these mountains, was a frequent visitor to this mine. When the countless pieces of the jar were painstakingly superglued together only a few small fragments were amiss and the finished article is shown on page 104.

No plans of the Glenariff Mines are known to exist and their extent may therefore never now be known but at least they can claim that the mineral railway which served them gave birth to the Irish Narrow Gauge (see also chapter on the Glenariff Mineral Railway).

THE CARGAN TRACT

Situated at Cargan village, these mines played an important part in the story of the mining industry for it was here that the association of bauxite with iron ore was discovered in 1871 by J.F.W. Hodges. There is some difference of opinion as to what company actually opened the mines but it appears most likely to have been the Antrim Iron Ore Company who worked them from the late 1860's to 1882 and thereafter by the Crommelin Mining Company.

The ore was good quality, up to 40% iron falling to 18% in the poorer seams, and the mined ore was for a time transported to Red Bay on the Wire Tramway and later by rail to Belfast. There was a noticeable dip in these mines which caused extensive flooding in the lower sections though the actual abandonment by the Antrim Co. in 1882 was attributed to the presence of numerous volcanic dykes which terminated the ore seam. From then on this company turned its attention to the Dungonnell area (see letter in Appendix 1) and Cargan Mines came into the possession of the British Aluminium Company who leased them later on to the Crommelin Company who worked the iron ore and bauxite for a number of years.

There were two separate mines at Cargan, served by five adits. It appears that adits 1, 2 and 3 were certainly closed by 1907 and a dozen men were still employed at the other mine, i.e. adits 4 and 5, where they were trying to relieve the mine of water but by the following year this mine too was closed. This mine is now completely blocked but a constant spring of fresh, clear water issues from it which often quenched many's a thirst in Cargan before the coming of the 'dam'. The other mine was, till December 1982, accessible via a 'back door' and was one of the author's favourite mines before a bulldozer obliterated it. It contains many interesting features, mainly high and wide roadways, inclined passages, high-level workings, coffin levels (from the shape of the passage), large calcite and aragonite crystals and deep water in places and remains of another poteen still.

THE DUNGONNELL TRACT

These mines, opened by the Antrim Iron Ore Company about 1887, lie in the valley of the Ballsallagh Water near the fort of Dungonnell in the vicinity of the Dungonnell Dam. The ore was good quality but even so mining ceased in 1891 because of disagreements between the company and the lease holders. These mines too were subject to flooding. A short railway linked them to Cargan station via the Cargan Mines. The Author examined the one level which was still open in the late 1980s but due to exceptionally deep water and a dipping roof no further exploration was carried out.

THE MOUNTCASHEL MINES

South west from Dungonnell along the slopes of Carncormick in the townlands of Evishnablay, Crooknahaya and Gortnageeragh are the group of mines known as the Mountcashel Mines or locally as the Bleagh Mines. They were opened about 1872 by a family called Holloway and mined by the Mountcashel Iron Ore Company who represented the Ebbw Vale Iron and Steel Company of South Wales. The ore was dressed at the mines near the mearing of the first two townlands where the ruins of the wash house, settling ponds and crusher still remain and then removed via the mineral railway to Knockanully Station situated at 350 feet lower altitude (see also the Chapter on Mining Methods). There may also have been a weighbridge and magazine.

The problem of drainage here was a considerable obstacle to profitable mining and attempts were made to drain the mines of water to avoid closure in 1908. This was achieved by driving a drainage tunnel for 900 feet into the mines which helped to stave off closure till 1923. This drainage level is still open though gated and is used as a private source of water. This is the only one of these mines to have been examined by the author as well as some surface examination of the state of the adits and no plans are known to exist. The average yield of the good ore was about 40% decreasing to 17% in the poorer seams.

THE RATHKENNY MINES

Situated east of the former Rathkenny creamery, about five miles from Ballymena, these mines were opened in late 1875 by the Antrim Iron Ore Company. The mining tract comprises the townlands of Rathkenny, Carncoagh and part of Killygore with ore being proved also below Craigywarren Bog and east of Braeside. The average quality of the No.1 ore was between 42 and 44%, i.e. higher than in the Parkmore Mine, and averaged about 14 inches in thickness. The mined ore was taken to the surface via a shaft located about halfway between Rathkenny Lower and Carncoagh Lower and thence to Rathkenny Station via a short siding. The ore bed in this mine was traversed by numerous basalt dykes, two of which can still be seen crossing the main artery of the mine east of Rathkenny Upper. In this area can also be found an unusually thick seam of lignite with an abundance of fossilised wood and one particularly long tree trunk in the roof. The lignite replaces and obliterates all traces of the iron ore seam and there is a complete absence of iron colouration in the surrounding rock. Perhaps it was because of this lignite that a coal-cutting machine was used at Rathkenny.

It was initially thought that this lignite seam accounted for the presence of foul air which the author experienced on his first visit to the mine on 1st May 1976. However, on numerous occasions since that date it was noticed that the air in the area of the lignite seam had deteriorated gradually up to a point where the roadway inclines upwards, beyond which breathing apparatus is now required in order to proceed. Strangely enough, no foul air has ever been experienced in any of the other mines explored and where no lignite exists. Perhaps the fact that the only access to this mine is via a vertical shaft which has a manhole cover suggests that the air is bad because normally the shaft is airtight and fresh air can therefore not circulate.

Serious drainage difficulties were encountered in these mines in the first decade of the 20th century and drainage tunnels were driven to rid the mines of water. Mining ceased at Rathkenny in 1922 and no plans of the workings are known to exist but explorations in the mine prove that an extensive network of roadways lie beneath the eastern portions of Rathkenny and Carncoagh townlands.

The original vertical shaft to the mine is now filled up due to the fact that many years ago a horse fell down it. The present entrance to the mine is down a brick-lined, laddered shaft 30ft deep, which was driven by a local farmer in search of water and which broke into the mine workings. A somewhat similar event when the mine itself was being worked is the subject of a humourous story. It appears that a well was sunk in the farmyard of a certain Mr. Turtle of Rathkenny Upper and the bottom of the well terminated directly beside and a little below the floor level of the mine passage. Whether the well was sunk before the mine was driven or vice versa is immaterial but at any rate the miners became aware of the proximity of the well and when the bucket came down for water the miners would grab hold of it and fill it with stones before it started on its upward journey again. No doubt the man at the top of the well did not appreciate the joke, the feasibility of which was confirmed when the author visited the mine in 1976. The shaft of the well is separated from the mine roadway by only a few inches of rock. A square hole, about 18 inches across, has been cut in the wall into the shaft so that it is possible to look up the well from the bottom. The well is now piped for a pump and the mine at this point is running in the direction of a disused level at Killygore.

This mine is one of the few in the area in which you can walk upright for long distances.

OTHER TRACTS

Apart from all the above-mentioned mines there were other workings situated further east of Rathkenny on the southern side of the Longmore Road. These comprised the mines of Coreen, Knockboy (abandoned 1880), Clonetrace, Elginny and Ballylig. The most important of these seems to have been the Elginny and Ballylig Mines which were formerly worked for iron ore, then closed for a time and re-opened in 1941 for bauxite. About 27,000 tons were removed from Elginny Mine in 1942. This was part of a large-scale re-investigation of bauxite reserves for the war effort and resulted in new mines being opened at Skerry East, Newtowncrommelin and Ballynabarnish and Lyle's Hill, Templepatrick. Prior to 1873 several excavations to test the ore bed had been made at Templepatrick and a suggestion made that the ore could be worked by underground mining but it wasn't until World War Two that this was put into practice. The mines at Skerry, Elginny and Ballylig finally closed early in 1944 while Ballynabarnish and Lyle's Hill were abandoned on 31.12.45.

Sources:
The Interbasaltic Rocks (Iron Ores & Bauxites) of N.E.Ireland, by GAJ Cole et al, Memoirs Geological Survey, Dublin HMSO, 1912.
Crommelin Mining Co. Ltd., Memorandum and Articles of Association, 9th January 1888 – Author's Collection.
Information from the Mineral Development Branch, former Dept. of Commerce, N.I.
The Iron Mines of Antrim, R A Watson, Dublin University Magazine Vol 83, 1874.

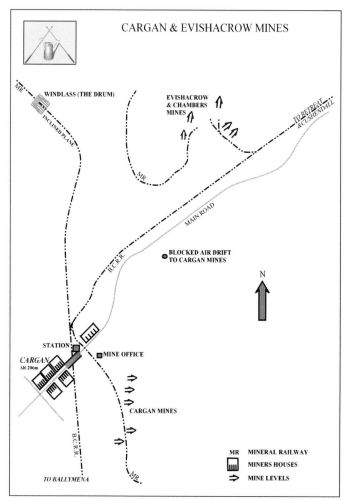

CARGAN & EVISHACROW MINES

MR

WINDLASS (THE DRUM)

INCLINED PLANE

EVISHACROW
& CHAMBERS
MINES

TO RETREAT
& CUSHENDALL

MR

MAIN ROAD

B.C.R.R.

BLOCKED AIR DRIFT
TO CARGAN MINES

N

STATION

CARGAN
Alt 206m

MINE OFFICE

CARGAN MINES

B.C.R.R.

MR

TO BALLYMENA

MR   MINERAL RAILWAY

    MINERS HOUSES

    MINE LEVELS

Map showing the Cargan and Evishacrow mines

Mountcashel Drainage Adit

Mountcashel Mines mineral railway

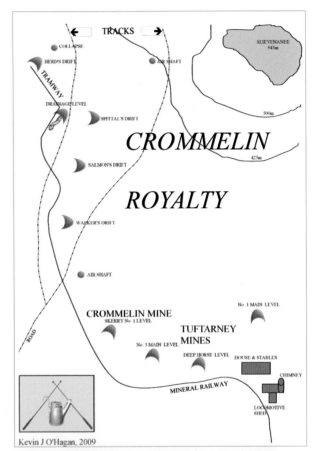

TRACKS

COLLAPSE

HERD'S DRIFT

TRAMWAY

AIR SHAFT

SLIEVENANEE
543m

DRAINAGE LEVEL

SPITTAL'S DRIFT

CROMMELIN

500m

425m

SALMON'S DRIFT

ROYALTY

WALKER'S DRIFT

AIR SHAFT

ROAD

CROMMELIN MINE
SKERRY No. 1 LEVEL

No. 3 MAIN LEVEL

TUFTARNEY
MINES

No. 1 MAIN LEVEL

DEEP HORSE LEVEL

HOUSE & STABLES

CHIMNEY

MINERAL RAILWAY

LOCOMOTIVE
SHED

Kevin J O'Hagan, 2009

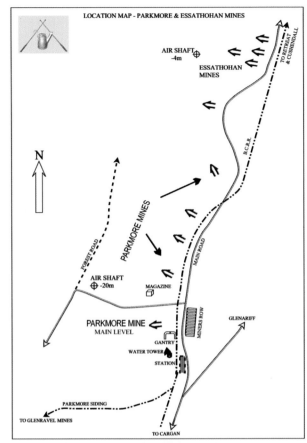

LOCATION MAP - PARKMORE & ESSATHOHAN MINES

AIR SHAFT
-4m

ESSATHOHAN
MINES

TO RETREAT
& CUSHENDALL

B.C.R.R.

N

PARKMORE MINES

FOREST ROAD

AIR SHAFT
-20m

MAGAZINE

MAIN ROAD

MINERS ROW

GLENARIFF

PARKMORE MINE
MAIN LEVEL

GANTRY

WATER TOWER

STATION

PARKMORE SIDING

TO GLENRAVEL MINES

TO CARGAN

Above: Maps showing the Crommelin and Parkmore Mines

Evishacrow Mine ◄

Essathohan Mine (Midgey Corner) ►

Chapter Seven
The Ballymena, Cushendall
and Red Bay Railway

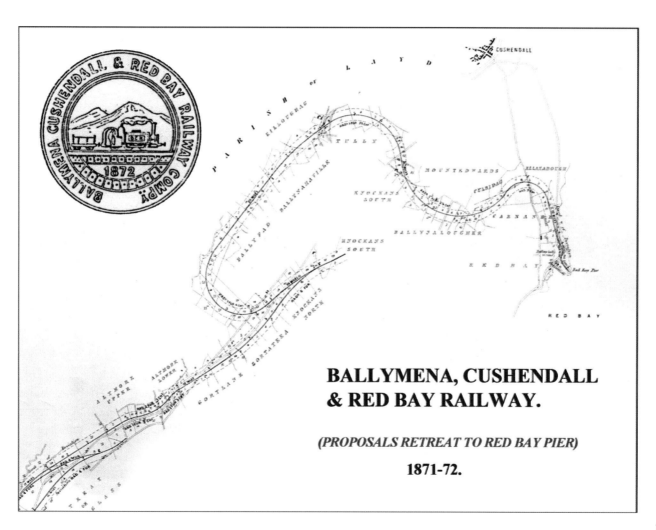

BALLYMENA, CUSHENDALL
& RED BAY RAILWAY.

(PROPOSALS RETREAT TO RED BAY PIER)

1871-72.

With the opening and expansion of the iron ore mines of mid-Antrim in the late 1860s, an industry which spread rapidly and encompassed most of the high ground in the county where Upper Basalt occurs, the mining companies quickly realised the urgency of suitable land transport for removal of the large tonnages of ore for export. Most of the mines were within a short distance of the sea with numerous bays where good harbour facilities could be constructed. Those further inland were nearer to the provincial towns from which railways ran to the larger sea ports. It was to take nine years, however, from the commencement of mining before a railway was built which would serve the largest concentration of workings in the Glenravel/Parkmore area. In the interim, various other modes of transport were utilised, initially cartage by horse and cart, the Wire Tramway, the private railways which served the Glenariff and Trostan Mines and, even in some cases, traction engines.

The original intention was that the line would be laid down Ballyeamon Glen and via the outskirts of Cushendall to Red Bay pier (see plan overleaf). However, this did not in the end materialise due to the severe gradients down the glen and the impossibility of a locomotive being able to haul wagons up those same gradients. This was a great disappointment to the inhabitants of the area at the time and although the line never reached its intended target it seems that the business and professional men of the period always had the question of a connection to Cushendall in the back of their minds.

Although the Glenariff mineral railway was the first narrow gauge system in Ireland it was a private railway for the conveyance of ore only and as such did not require parliamentary approval for its construction. The B.C.R.R. on the other hand did require such approval and thereby became the first government approved narrow gauge railway in the country. The company was incorporated on 18th July 1872, initially to carry freight between Ballymena and Cushendall, and the first section of line from Ballymena to Cargan, a distance by rail of 11.75 miles, was opened on 26th May 1875. A further 4.75 miles to Retreat were opened on 8th October 1876 and between Cargan and Retreat the railway attained a height of 1,045 feet at Essathohan, becoming the highest rail point in Ireland. Although the original terminus was Red Bay pier, the line was never laid since the gradient beyond Retreat was too steep and would have involved a long reversing curve to negotiate the descent. This would have added greatly to the cost and although several plans were considered none were utilised.

The coming of the railway greatly facilitated the transport of ore from the mines. Branches were laid to the individual groups of mines, namely Bleagh, Cargan, Dungonnell, Evishacrow and Parkmore.

These became known respectively as the Mountcashel Mineral Railway, Cargan Siding, Dungonnell Mineral Railway, Evishacrow Siding and Parkmore Siding. The Crommelin Mineral Railway served the mines on the western side of Slievenanee and linked to Cargan station via 'the Drum'. Another railway ran from Ballynahavla Bridge to the upper levels of the Evishacrow Mines and another served the mines on the south slope of Slievenanee. The latter was in fact Fisher's Tramway, built by James Fisher in 1866 for use initially by horse-drawn wagons, which preceded the narrow gauge steam-driven system. The section from Ballynahavla Bridge to Parkmore Station was laid following the coming of the B.C.R.R. and became known as the Parkmore Siding.

Up to 1880 ore from the mines had to be transferred to other wagons on the broad gauge line at Ballymena but on 22nd September of that year a link with the Ballymena and Larne narrow gauge system at Harryville enabled the ore to be carried direct from the mines to Lame Harbour without stop.

Traffic on the B.C.R.R, was never very heavy and from 1880 (its busiest year) onwards it gradually declined. The company was subsequently taken over by the Belfast and Northern Counties Railway on 14th July 1884 (date of Royal Assent) and passenger traffic was commenced an 5th April 1886 to Knockanully station and to Parkmore on 27th August 1888. For this purpose a red brick, two-storey stationmaster's house was constructed plus waiting rooms and a refreshment room. Unfortunately, none of these now remain. In 1903 the Midland Railway (Northern Counties Committee) took over the line and made a few improvements. Iron ore production revived during the first World War and in 1915 the Antrim Iron Ore Co. sought reinstatement of the disused Mountcashel branch line, which was completed in 1916. During the 'troubles' of the 1920's the stations at Crossroads, Cargan, Parkmore and Retreat were burnt down. The passenger accommodation at Parkmore was replaced with a pre-fabricated, reinforced concrete building, most of which still remains in poor repair. The name PARKMORE is still in place above the door, opposite the former platform. Just a short distance from the terminus stands a fine, square water tank with its iron ladder intact and the name of the manufacturer, James Moore Belfast 1906, plainly visible front and rear. Between the tank and the site of the station master's house, a few yards to the north, was the garden where various items of cutlery have been found along with evidence that the area was used for target practice during the last War.

Parkmore
Station

Parkmore
invoice for iron
ore shipments

In April 1891 the BNCR wrote to the Crommelin Mining Co. asking if they would give, free of charge, a narrow strip of land - 230 feet by 12 feet - for the construction of a passenger station (platform and signal box) at Cargan, behind the goods shed. This was in response to a request from the residents of Cargan as it would be of advantage to them now that the line was open to passenger traffic. The land was subsequently given and a conveyance drawn up in October of that year, subject to a yearly rent of five shillings. (Cumbria Record Office, DH 115/1/2/2).

From 1923 the Midland became part and parcel of the much larger London, Midland and Scottish Railway operating through the Northern Counties Committee but by this time, with Britain getting back on its feet after war shortages and restrictions, the railways were faced with heavy competition from other modes of transport. Passengers and business users were happier to pay the lower fares for road transport and traffic on the Ballymena line dwindled even further than it had been already doing.

Passengers were not taken beyond Parkmore but passenger traffic continued up to 1930 when in September of that year it finally ceased and the building at Parkmore became a Youth Hostel for a time. On 17th April 1937 the last 10 miles of track between Rathkenny and Retreat were removed. The line to Rathkenny was retained for the benefit of the creamery but in 1940 the remaining track from Ballymena was lifted. So ended an era of Irish railway history. In its heyday Parkmore was the highest railway station in Ireland.

Sources:
The Ballymena Lines, E.M. Patterson, 1968.
The Proposed Larne to Parkmore Light Railway, K.J. O'Hagan, The Glynns 2006.
Ballymena, Cushendall and Red Bay Railway, Engineer's Plans, 1871/72 Session, (in Author's possession).
Photographs – Author.

Chapter Eight
Cargan to Red Bay
Wire Tramway

Wire tramway terminus

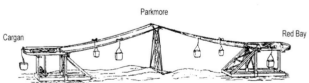

Plan of wire tramway route from Cargan to Red Bay ▲

Hodgson's principle of wire rope transport ➤

Before the coming of the narrow gauge railway to north east Antrim iron ore was being mined extensively in the Glenravel hills with further trials being carried out at the Trostan Mines for bauxite. James Fisher, who had opened the mines in 1866, had built his own tramway for use by horse-drawn wagons from his mines in the townland of Legagrane to the nearest suitable road at Parkmore and thence by horse and cart to Red Bay pier. For the other mining companies the problem of transporting the ore was more difficult. They were further from the sea and the nearest main railway was at Ballymena but roads were only muddy tracks suitable for horse and cart and the carting of heavy loads especially in winter was slow, expensive and at times even impossible. Since the sea lay only a few miles away, with the sheltered harbour of Red Bay available for shipping, it seemed logical and sensible to transport the ore there for shipment. The alternative was a long and costly roundabout journey to Belfast via Ballymena.

So it was in 1871 the Antrim Wire Tramway Company was formed (a subsidiary of the Wire Tramway Co. of London) to lay out the course of an overhead bucket system between Cargan and Red Bay via Retreat. The course, about 8 miles long, was to be based on Charles Hodgson's system of wire rope transport patented in 1868 and was to run through the townlands of Cargan, Evishacrow and Parkmore then to Essathohan and down Ballyeamon Glen through Knockans North, Ballynalougher to Red Bay. It would consist of an endless wire rope, supported on a series of pulleys and revolving round a horizontal wheel at each end and the whole lot carried on wooden pylons. The rope would be passed round a drum driven by a steam engine situated at Knockans.

Aerial wire ropeways provided a cheap means of transport for ore without the necessity of preparing a track along the ground. The ore is carried in buckets, supported clear of the ground by wire ropes, upheld at intervals by standards or pylons. The use of a single rope was first made a practicable means of conveyance by Hodgson in 1868, and was improved by Hallidie and others. As at that time arranged, an endless steel wire rope is passed around two horizontal drums, one at each end, forming two parallel lines of rope, about six or eight feet apart. These are supported, at intervals of about 200 feet or so, upon vertical pylons from 15 to 20 feet high. Generally speaking, the average gradient for such a self-acting ropeway must not be less than about 1 in 6. The loaded buckets are connected to the running rope by means of gripping saddles, or by means of clips, permanently attached to the rope. Only a moderate rope speed can be used – about two miles per hour, while the loads carried are only about 2 to 3cwt. each.

Before work on this aerial ropeway actually started the railway was planned which was to run through the heart of the mining area.

The wire tramway was eventually started and completed in 1872. There were four sections each two miles long and the wire rope and pulleys were supported by 50 pylons per section. The main engine was a 20hp steam engine at Knockans with a 10hp engine at Evishacrow Grand Junction Station where there was a short offshoot towards the Evishacrow Mines. The tramway carried 200 buckets each with a capacity of two and a half hundredweight. The full ones went down one side and the empties came up the other and the average speed of the system was 4mph. About 200 tons of ore per day were transported on the wire tramway but the enterprise itself was short-lived for on the night of Sunday July 13th, 1873 the wire rope was severed at a point just north of Essathohan Bridge thus crippling the entire mechanism.

At the time it was thought the carters were to blame as the construction of the tramway would have deprived them of their livelihood. On the other hand the railway company which was in the process of planning the narrow gauge line stood to lose much by the competition of the tramway. The fact that the sabotage had occurred on July 13th may have had a political significance but the other reasons seem more plausible. There had been a previous attempt to wreck the tramway when large stone blocks had been rolled down the mountain from the chalk quarry high on the slopes of Lurigethan. This had resulted in a law suit. The cutting of the wire rope on the other hand meant that the tramway was put completely out of action and never ran again.

Two weeks later, 26th July 1873, the reward notice shown below appeared in the Ballymena Observer and was displayed elsewhere throughout the area:

In the same issue of 26th July a lengthy condemnation of the outrage appeared on the front page, strangely reminiscent one might add, of condemnations of similar activities in our own time.

Under the heading 'Diabolical Outrage' it reads as follows:

"From our advertising column it will be seen that a most disgraceful outrage – one of a character hitherto without precedent among the peaceable and industrious population of this Province – was wantonly perpetrated at Parkmore, near Red Bay, in the County of Antrim, on the night of Sunday the

13th inst. On that night it appears that the massive wire rope of the Wire Tramway, constructed for the conveyance of ore from the iron mines at Cargan to Red Bay pier, was maliciously cut asunder by some person or persons at present unknown, whereby the traffic along the entire line, extending over a distance of about a dozen miles, was necessarily suspended. The tramway – which is the property of a London company - must have cost several thousand pounds and it has been in full operation for months past, doing important service in aid of a patriotic effort to develop the natural resources of our country, and provide remunerative employment for the people. An act of more atrocious malignity has not been perpetrated in this district of County Antrim within the present century; and, in view of this suicidal tendency among the Irish peasantry, it cannot be thought strange if Englishmen hesitate to invest their capital, or carry out their mercantile enterprise, among a people many of whom appear to be labouring under the heavy curse of a national blindness. The Company have offered a reward of One Hundred Pounds for such information as shall lead to the discovery of the offenders, and if clearly convicted, penal servitude for years is the lightest punishment they can expect. It should be known that every shilling's worth of the damage inflicted, as well as every shilling's worth of the concurrent loss, is recoverable by county assessment upon the cesspayers of the several townlands over which the tramway passes; and the well-disposed inhabitants should unite as one man in the public denunciation of these doings, and for the prompt suppression of such shameful practices. An additional reward by voluntary contributions should be offered for the apprehension and conviction of the guilty parties, and every honest man in the Glens should be a subscriber to the fund."

Ballymena Observer
26th July 1873

This act of wanton sabotage put the wire tramway completely out of action and it remained so until 1875 when the whole concern was sold to the railway company which by this time was operating to Cargan Station. The Wire Tramway Company claimed damages of £1,000 for their loss but the culprits were apparently never found, only their footprints. The BCRR's original offer of £11,000 in 1873 had been turned down by the tramway company but by 1875 the price had dropped to £500. The Retreat to Red Bay section of the tramway was kept in position although it was derelict, and a caretaker was employed by the BCRR to look after it. It was thought that this section could still be adapted to carry ore from Retreat to Red Bay and the BCRR even ordered new wire rope but the plan was abandoned and the whole concern was sold in 1881.

An interesting story connected with the tramway concerns an incident at Jenny's Bar, on the roadside just above Cargan (now a sheep pen). Apparently, there was a fight in which a man was fatally injured with a bull-whip. Before the police could arrive the killer ran off and, climbing into one of the buckets of the tramway, was conveyed safely to Red Bay pier from which he eventually made his escape by boat.

In the week following the demise of the tramway the Belfast Naturalist's Field Club visited the area to see this ingenuous method of transport for themselves. They were shown the tramway near Parkmore but in their journal later no mention was made of the fact that the system had been damaged. Perhaps this fact had been deliberately kept from them by the guide who had described its working. It may even have been that the Company thought that a simple thing like a wire rope could easily be replaced and that the tramway would soon be back in action but sadly this was not to be and this unique piece of engineering lapsed into history.

The picture above shows the tramway's Red Bay terminus alongside the final cable-carrying pylon with the Red Arch in the background. The wooden bridge over the Coast Road was to protect traffic passing below from any ore which might spill out of the moving buckets before they entered the wheelhouse. As the buckets passed round the revolving horizontal wheel their contents were tipped sideways into a chute and thence to the ground below. One of the buildings on the right was for stabling the horses which were used on the pier. On the road below the bridge can be seen a horse and cart near an upturned cart and another horse at a lower level. In the centre of the tower is a sign inscribed 'WIRE TRAMWAY CO. LIMITED'.

Although no other photographs of the tramway exist, it would have been very similar in construction to the ones which served the Ben Bulben barytes mines and the Arigna coal mines. The Ben Bulben one can still be seen, the Arigna one has now, unfortunately, been dismantled.

Sources:
Photo of the Wire Tramway terminus, courtesy of Mrs Myoko Turnley, Drumnasole House.
Proceedings of the Belfast Naturalists Field Club, 1864-1880, July 1873.
Ballymena Observer, 26th July 1873, 29th January 1976.
The Harmsworth Encyclopaedia, Vol VII, circa 1910.
Information from the late Jack McCann and the late Jimmy Irvine.

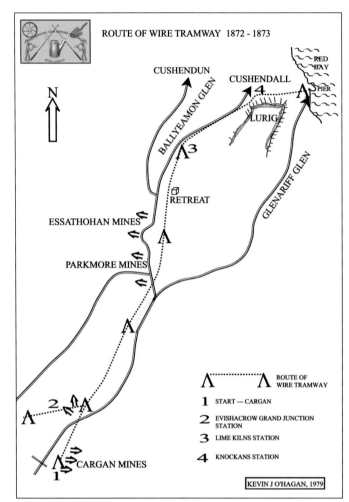

Map showing the route of the wire tramway

Reward poster

Chapter Nine
The Inclined plane
at Cargan (The Drum)

*Reconstruction
of the Drum*

"The waggons descend along an inclined plane of two hundred and sixty yards in length, and of remarkable declivity, especially towards the lower extremity; the distance is traversed in one minute and a half, the full waggons being made to draw up the empty ones: on some days, upwards of three hundred pass by this route.

"At the summit of the inclined plane, an admirable contrivance is resorted to, in aid of the brake wheel, than which there was formerly no other implement to counteract the force of the laden waggons on their descent: the weight of these, however, not being sufficiently compensated by the empty ones ascending at the same time, the stress on the brake was consequently very formidable; and this stress it was the object to remedy. The pistons of two large air-cylinders, connected by cranks to the axle round which the rope that sustains the descending waggons is coiled, are so constructed, that, acting immediately upon the axle, they oppose an equable force to its revolution, and retard the waggons in their progress down: nay, to such a degree, as to stop them altogether, were it not that the man in charge has the means of regulating their force, by allowing the air to escape in any degree he thinks proper. This person is continually ready at his post, having a handle connected with the valve within his reach, as well as continual hold on the pole of the brake. The force opposed to the axle is rendered equable by the alternate motion of the pistons; as one of these ascends, the other descends, thus relieving one another; that is to say, as the piston of each air-cylinder descends, the valve opens; as it ascends, it shuts, thereby throwing the resistance upon the axle: no sooner, therefore, is one piston hors de combat, than the other resumes the labour, and thus, both working alternately one after the other, the same force, neither more nor less, is in continual action.

"The above operation refers to the last two hundred and sixty yards of the distance performed by the waggons; the preceding half mile, in the same direction, is along a railroad, on a level, whence the waggons are drawn by horses." [1].

The above account relates to the operation of an inclined plane near Whitehaven in Cumbria in 1835. The Crommelin Iron Ore Company, who operated the Evishacrow inclined plane, were from Dalton-in-Furness and would therefore have been familiar with the operation of other mines in the locality. As well, the use of inclined planes for transporting ore in mountainous areas is a common practice and many examples of them remain today, particularly in Wales, and traces of others can still be seen in Co. Antrim. It is likely, therefore, that the above account reflects closely the operation of the inclined plane at Evishacrow, with one important difference in the method of braking.

Instead of using air-cylinders, a large band-brake on the windlass was used. This would have been operated by the brakeman using a long lever which provided considerable braking power.

It was the Antrim Iron Ore Co. that first took out a lease to mine for iron ore in the townland of Tuftarney and to construct a tramway. The lease between the company and the Earl of Antrim was dated 1st May 1873 and was for 21 years. A few years later (1875-1876) other parcels of land in the townlands of Cargan and Legagrane were leased for the construction of a tramway to link with the Earl of Antrim's lands. This link would have been via what is now known as the Drum Brae. By this time the narrow gauge railway had arrived in Cargan (May 1875). The Antrim Iron Ore Co. then re-leased and assigned some of its lands to the Ballymena, Cushendall & Red Bay Railway Co. and William Crossley, an ironmaster from Dalton-in-Furness. He immediately formed a partnership with George Bargate from the same town and they became the Crommelin Iron Ore Co. in 1876. It is likely that the Drum dates from this same year since it could not have operated prior to 1875.

Within a few years, however, the Crommelin company was in financial difficulty and the mineral railway and Drum were put up for auction in Belfast in December 1880. The auction sale notice comprised the lands, railway, engine house and other buildings including stables and the house commonly known as Warnocks and the windlass, i.e. the Drum. The whole lot was described as in complete working order.[2] The sale did not include the Crommelin company's locomotive which was a Fox Walker, three feet gauge engine. Presumably this was kept in the large engine house, situated at Tuftarney, above the present-day cattle grid. The locomotive was sold in 1882 to the Belfast Harbour Commissioners who were undertaking land reclamation on the foreshore at Belfast Lough at the time.

As it happened, however, the Drum and railway were not sold at auction and lay idle for some years, eventually falling into disrepair. They were eventually bought by a second Crommelin company – the Crommelin Mining Co. Ltd which took over the liabilities of the former company in 1888. This company had been formed in January 1888 with a capital of £30,000. It had no connection with the former company and had its offices in Whitehaven, Lancashire – quite a distance from Dalton-in-Furness.[3] The new company had to spend over £900 in respect of repairs to the railway and accoutrements and over £300 in wages as well as open new mines, purchase another locomotive and pay the miners. By the time they had paid off all this and the former company's debts as well they hadn't much left but did manage to continue in existence until 1934.

The Crommelin Mining Co. Ltd commenced operations in Glenravel in 1888, working an extensive tract in the townlands of Skerry East and Tuftarney. Later, they also took over the Evishacrow and Chambers Mines and the Cargan and Parkmore Mines. They now had their own mineral railway along the south western flank of Slievenanee from Herd's Drift to Cargan Station via the Drum Brae. They had two locomotives which were housed in the engine shed at the Skerry East - Legagrane boundary (near the cattle grid on the road to Ballynahavla) and a water tank, the walls of which still remain. The track ran south eastwards from the cattle grid towards the Drum walls and thence to Cargan. Just before reaching the walls there was a sandpit, a safety feature in the event of runaway wagons, and a double line of rails to act as a passing place and for wagons waiting for dispatch down the incline. The incline itself had twin tracks to facilitate the up and down movement of wagons, three loaded wagons going down being sufficient to pull 10 empties up.

Locomotive of the Crommelin Iron Ore Co, built 1878

The Drum itself consisted of two upright walls, slightly inclined inwards, between which was the huge windlass wound with steel rope. As the loaded wagons went down the incline the drum revolved thus drawing the empties upwards. The structure would have been roofed to keep out the worst effects of the weather and though the walls still remain they are now in a sorry state. The brakeman would have been positioned near the top of the incline to enable him to attach the wagons to the rope and to see them coming and going on the slope. The double track merged into one after levelling off at the bottom of the incline.

The Drum Walls are situated about 912 feet above sea level and the gradient of the incline is 1 in 11. The bottom of the incline is about 720 feet above sea level. This makes the length of the incline about 423 feet.

A story is also told of the engine driver coming out of Cargan Station who must have had a rough night or wasn't concentrating. He ran his locomotive up to the foot of the Drum Brae as usual but forgot to stop and nosed his engine up the brae before the steepness of the incline stopped it.

Sources:
1. A Home Tour through the manufacturing districts of England , Scotland and Ireland, Vol 1, Sir George Head, 1840.
2. Information from Cumbria Record Office, Whitehaven.
3. Articles of Association, Crommelin Mining Co. Ltd., Author's collection.
4. Image - Locomotive of the Crommelin Iron Ore Co., Courtesy of Andrew J Waldron, Lostock, Lancashire.

The Drum Brae

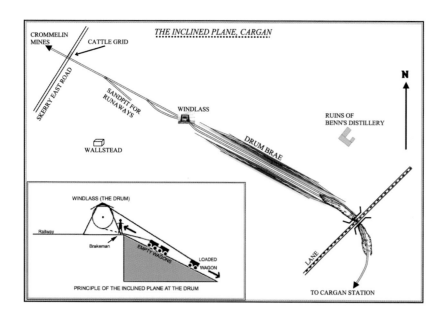

Diagram showing an overview of the inclined plane at Cargan

THE INCLINED PLANE, CARGAN

CROMMELIN MINES

CATTLE GRID

SKERRY EAST ROAD

SANDPIT FOR RUNAWAYS

WINDLASS

WALLSTEAD

DRUM BRAE

RUINS OF BENN'S DISTILLERY

N

LANE

TO CARGAN STATION

WINDLASS (THE DRUM)

Railway

Brakeman

EMPTY WAGONS

LOADED WAGON

PRINCIPLE OF THE INCLINED PLANE AT THE DRUM

The ruins of the Drum walls

Chapter Ten
Glenariff Mineral Railway

The Glenariff Iron ore and
Harbour Co. pier Red Bay

The mining of iron ore in the Glenravel area, which commenced in 1866, quickly mushroomed throughout the surrounding district with new companies being formed to open out the surrounding hills. By early 1873 mining was being carried on at several locations in Glenravel and about this time the Glenariff Iron Ore and Harbour Company was incorporated to mine ore in the Glenariff tract. Their capital was £130,000 in 13,000 shares of £10 each and two leases were acquired from the Earl of Antrim for mining the ore and to construct the pier and railway. These leases comprised over 6,500 acres, of which 5,200 acres were reckoned as containing about 20million tons of ore. The tract comprised all the townlands down the glen from Cloughcorr to Bay between the east bank of the Glenariff River and the cliffs and from Waterfoot to the Bay Chapel. The four Directors were all London-based and the Secretary was John Ham.[1]

These mines were opened on 1st November 1873 and lasted in all about nine years. The most productive years were 1877 and 1878 when 17,857 tons and 25,527 tons respectively of first quality ore were mined, well short of the 100,000 tons expected per annum, along with smaller tonnages of second quality ore. Production declined the following year and reached another peak in 1880 when nearly 16,000 tons were mined, but the following year just under 9,500 tons were raised and mining was at an end.[2] Miners were brought over from Scotland and England to work these mines.

Evidence suggests that the area between Glenariff and the valley of the Cranny Water at Carnlough is not very promising and it is remarkable too that between the mines of the Inver Gorge and the wealthy Parkmore tract, a mile and a half distant, no ore was found after trial borings.

White Arch
◄

Greenheart supports on the foreshore
►

The Glenariff Mines, therefore, were completely isolated from all the other mining areas and there was neither a direct road link to the coast or to Parkmore, nor, in 1873, any railway to Ballymena. A pier had been built on the northern shore of Red Bay in 1849 but it was not convenient to the mines. For this reason and to avoid a long and costly overland journey to Ballymena the company decided that it would be wiser and cheaper to build their own railway to the coast and a pier to provide a means of getting the ore away quickly. Work began on these in the Spring of 1873 and since it was a private venture for the sole purpose of transporting minerals no parliamentary approval was necessary, only the permission of the landowners along the route. The railway was opened in 1873 with a three feet gauge and gave birth to the Irish narrow gauge system. It was envisaged by the Company that the pier would enable 100,000 tons of ore to be shipped in the first year or two, rising to 1,000 tons per day, (300,000 per year), but neither target was ever achieved nor could they have been realistic. The total value of the ore actually mined was £66,000, just over half of the company's capital.[3]

Although the sea was only four miles away the total length of track was nearly six miles. This included sidings and a zigzag section near the mines since these lay at a higher level than the main track. The gradient of the system was 1 in 40 and other features were the Greenaghan Viaduct, a seventy-foot high bridge over the gorge of the Altmore Burn, and the White Arch where it crossed over the Coast Road.

From here it ran on a trestle supported by uprights of greenheart timber and alongside the ore chutes on the pier which was made of concrete with timber superstructure. This pier was completed in 1874 and provided a minimum depth of twenty-five feet alongside the greater part of it. Here vessels of up to 2000 tons could berth safely but owing to its exposed position it was only possible to load the ore during calm weather. Cargoes of mined ore were shipped mainly to the Bristol Channel Ports.

The company's rolling stock consisted of two locomotives (some sources say four and another five) and forty-one wagons including a brake van, and 350 tons of rails were purchased from the copper mines in England. The engines were 2-4-0 tank type, built by Stephenson & Co. in 1873. They were sold in 1885 at the Sheriff's sale in Belfast to the Londonderry and Lough Swilly Railway Co. where they became their numbers five and six. For this they had to be manhandled to the Red Bay north pier as the Glenariff pier was by this time too weak to take their weight. They were eventually replaced by the L & L S Co. in 1899 and subsequently dismantled.

In an attempt to prolong the life of the railway a survey was carried out in 1880 on the possibility of linking the Glenariff railway with the Ballymena, Cushendall and Red Bay Railway at Parkmore. This new link was to be known as the Glenariff Junction Railway and was to be three miles long but owing to lack of capital the idea was abandoned in 1885.

Following the bankruptcy sale of 1885 the rails of the mineral railway were purchased on behalf of Lord Antrim and remained in place but in June 1890 about three miles of the track were stolen overnight, no mean feat since it would have involved a large gang of strong men toiling over several hours at back-breaking work, loading them into some sort of convevance, probably horse-drawn, and transporting them to some secret storage destination. The rails were presumably then sold but the theft resulted in a court appearance between the land owner and Lord Antrim at the Belfast Spring Assizes in 1891.[4] The company, itself, was eventually wound up in 1894. As if to put the final seal on this remarkable yet troubled enterprise the pier itself was washed away in a storm in the early hours of Tuesday 12th November 1901 - the night of another 'Big Wind'.

All that remains today are the broken remnants of the pier and the stubs of the greenheart trestle supports, the White Arch, the old engine shed which is now the Parochial Hall and Seaview Terrace, originally built for the miners and railway men. The course of the railway itself can still be plainly seen and is one of the forest park's walks. The Greenaghan Viaduct, built of white limestone pillars and with stout wooden beams to support the rails, was a masterpiece of engineering even by today's standards and still remains with every stone in place astride the gorge and waterfall of the Altmore Burn but hidden from view by thick vegetation. It is probably the most impressive relic of the mining era still in existence and well worth a visit if only to see the expert workmanship of the stonemasons and labourers who built it.

As for the mines themselves only one of these remains open but only for a short distance and there is little of interest for the would-be explorer, apart from the fact that evidence remains of its use by a well-known poteen maker. To remedy this it was decided in 1979 to re-open one of the blocked mines, with Forest Service approval, in the hope that some interesting and extensive workings might be discovered. The mine was explored in November 1979 but proved of little extent and appeared to be merely a trial adit for the purpose of locating a workable seam. No plans of the Glenariff Mines are known to exist and without them the full extent of these mines may never be known.

Glenariff Mineral Railway – zigzag section

The Glen itself was opened to tourists in July 1889 and two years later the tea-house at Laragh was opened to the public. Since then it has become a major tourist and rambling venue and with its incomparable scenic attraction and unique industrial history it is undoubtedly the finest of the State-owned forest parks.

Sources:
1. Glenariff Iron Ore & Harbour Co. Prospectus, 1873, Guildhall Library, London.
2. Mineral Statistics.
3. ibid.
4. Ballymena Observer, The Railway that Vanished, 29th January 1976, Jim Dowds & 4th March 1976, K J O'Hagan
Photo of Glenariff Pier, Courtesy of National Library of Ireland, ref: L_ROY_02311
See also Chapter on The Mining Tracts (The Glenariff Tract).

*Former engine
shed at Red Bay*

*Limestone
piers of the
Greenaghan
Viaduct*

Chapter 11
The Trostan Mineral Railway

*Artist's impression
of Trostan wagons*

Trostan Mineral Railway

Little is known of the Trostan Mines themselves but it appears that mining trials were commenced there in 1872 by the Antrim Iron Ore Co. and were still being carried on early in 1874. More than 20 adits were driven on the eastern and northern slopes of the mountain and some iron ore and bauxite were removed but the mines were of little extent inwardly and proved worthless.

A mineral railway was, however, built early in 1872 which eventually linked all the levels except for a few at the northern extremity which were probably the last to be driven. The railway or tramway was just under two miles long and terminated beside the present-day Ballyeamon Road about half a mile south west of Gault's Road and beside the course of the Wire Tramway which was completed in the same year. It is likely that ore was then carted to Red Bay pier rather than on the wire tramway since the latter would have involved stopping the system to fill the buckets and this would have meant a great deal of expense in providing machinery such as a gantry to fill the buckets without removing them from the wire rope. In any event the buckets on the wire rope would have been filled at the Cargan Mines and would have continued uninterrupted to Red Bay pier.

The Antrim Iron Ore Co., however, did propose to extend the tramway across the main Ballyeamon Road and alongside the BCRR, perhaps with the intention of loading the ore into BCRR wagons. From the plan below it is obvious that this was planned after the line to Retreat was completed (1876) but it was not pursued possibly because, within a short time, the mines themselves failed.

Since the mineral tramway itself preceded the coming of the steam driven trains to the area it was obviously a simple system for use with horse-drawn wagons. From the mines to the tramend there was a slight downhill gradient and it was only necessary to hitch four or five wagons together for them to run unaided to the

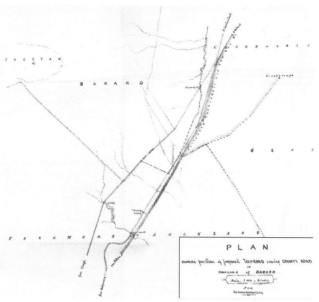

Plan showing part of the Trostan Mineral Railway and proposed road crossings

roadside. Unfortunately to return the empty wagons to the mines required the use of a horse, and horse and driver had to follow on foot behind the wagons in order to be there to haul them back. This double journey was found to be tiring for the horse so to overcome the problem it was decided to construct a small wagon to carry the horse and driver on the downward run, thus saving them a needless walk. It also meant that the horse could get by on a feed less a day. The sight of a horse and driver riding in an open wagon at the rear of several ore wagons and with no visible means of motive power must have been a rare sight indeed, even for the Glens in those days.

A similar system was later used (1887) by the Ontario & San Antonio Heights Railway Company. The story goes that after that line was electrified the mules employed were sold to a farmer and were excellent at pulling the plough uphill but refused to pull it downhill.

Sources:
The Iron Mines of Antrim, R A Watson, Dublin University Magazine Vol 83, 1874.
Plan for proposed Tramway Crossing, Author's Collection.
Ontario & San Antonio Heights Line, http://www.erha.org/pelines/peeosah.htm.

Selection of miners' bottles

Mickey McIlhatton's wine jar (for poteen making) found in Glenariff Mine

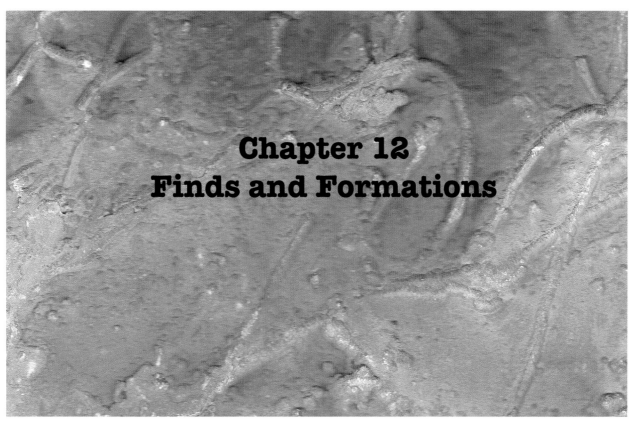

Chapter 12
Finds and Formations

Above:
Calcitised floor,
Salmon's Drift.

From far left:
Calcitised tin
can, cave pearls
and a collection
of clay pipes

One of the most rewarding aspects of exploring disused mines is the discovery of tools, implements and other articles which were used by the miners, to see their footprints and other personal items that they left behind, and the feeling of nearness to those men who left them. Another added attraction is the fact that some of the mines have been richly decorated by Nature with formations and deposits more common to caves, giving them an air of beauty and interrupting the uniformity which most mine passages tend to display.

To deal first of all with the natural formations it is necessary once again to return to the period of the deposition of the lavas. Because the mines were driven in the Interbasaltic Bed the overlying rock was naturally basalt. During the cooling process of the lavas which formed the Upper Basalt cavities were left in the rock called geodes. These cavities took the form of bubbles and cracks in the rock which were subsequently lined with crystals of the calcite group. In Salmon's Drift, for instance, huge crystals are plainly visible in the roof just above the first main road junction, and in the Cargan and Parkmore Mines similar large crystals occur. Calcite is dissolvable by contact with rain or surface water containing Carbon Dioxide and when this mixture again comes in contact with air such as in the roof of a cave or mine the dissolved calcite is deposited on the roof as Calcium Carbonate in the form of a stalactite or on the walls as flowstone. It is not surprising, therefore, to find in the mines these and many other formations. The calcite in the roof rock has been leached out by water percolating through cracks from the surface and has been redeposited in the mine passages in the manner described. Because the amount of calcite in the parent rock is small the resulting formations are equally small but none the less beautiful and on a scale comparable to the size of the mine passage itself. The stalactites occur mainly in clusters averaging half an inch long with a few as much as three inches (see Mountcashel). Stalactites, however, vary in their growth rates which depend on various factors and since the mines have only been opened for a hundred and fifty odd years the opportunity for fast growth has been rather small.

As well as these roof formations many of the mines display other forms of decoration such as flowstone on walls and floors. One section of passage in the Parkmore Mine has calcite-covered roof and walls which reflect a brilliant white in the light of the explorer's lamp. Most flowstone as seen in the Cargan, Glenravel, Salmon's Drift and Parkmore Mines is pure white but some deposits are tinted by the minerals through which they pass and orangey-red is, therefore, a common colour denoting the presence of iron. Dark blue and black are also found, coloured thus by the presence of manganese. Some passage floors contain calcite-rimmed pools with small white or toffee-coloured pebbles in them. Although not true 'cave pearls' these are formed in a similar manner, i.e. by the deposition of calcite around a tiny grain or chip of rock. The agitation of the water in the pool by drips from above allows tiny rock fragments in the pool to be covered completely by calcite and they eventually take on a rounded or oval shape.

The most decorated mine so far discovered is Salmon's Drift on the west side of Slievenanee. Here an unusually large deposit of calcite is to be seen. One passage, the Dyke Level, some distance into the mine and running slightly uphill, is completely floored with creamy white deposits with encrusted pools, calcite pearls and weird-shaped stone flowers. In a space of about 10 yards were found two hutch wheels, one shovel head, a timber prop and a tin can all covered in calcite of varying thickness. Some of the small pools of water are partly covered by floating calcite, evidence that it is continually forming. In the pools are strange worm-like shapes, criss-crossing each other as if they were living organisms or ancient fossils. These had originally been the black threads of fungus which can be seen growing from the rotting timbers. In the strongly calcitised environment the fine threads had been gradually covered with a coating of creamy calcite and had become beautiful though unusual formations.

It is impossible to walk in the passage without crunching and breaking these formations so it has been left undisturbed as much as possible. The walls and roof too are richly decorated, especially the latter, with an abundance of tiny white stalactites. The source of all this calcite is at the junction of two passages and stems from the roof above this junction. Pure black calcite covers the wall and part of the floor and merges into white as it progresses down the passage. Surprisingly, a few yards beyond this 'petrifying chamber' the rock becomes rather shattered and uneven as if a collapse had taken place and no exploration has been undertaken beyond this point.

When mining ceased very little of value was left behind in the mines. All tools, lamps, hutches and rails etc. were taken out because these items cost money and could be used elsewhere and so were worth salvaging. What was left was either broken or rusted useless, easily obtainable or of no other use. However, several interesting man-made articles have been found. These consist of different types and sizes of hutch wheel, the metal parts of hutches, mostly sides and hinges, rails and sleepers some still in situ, odd shaped bottles, earthenware jars and bits of delph, shovel heads and buckets and most interesting of all – clay pipes.

Quite a number of these have been found, some complete and some with stems broken and odd bits and pieces. Three of those found have intricately carved designs on their bowls. One shows a hand carved in relief on one side, generally mistaken as the Red Hand of Ulster, and a criss-crossed heart on the other side. The second is fashioned right round the bowl with a wicker basket design and this too is in relief. The third has a seven-pointed star on its bowl. Apart from decorating the pipes these designs served a useful purpose by providing a dry, rough surface on which to strike a match. The atmosphere in the mines is very humid and would have been more so when they were working. The miner's hands were invariably damp and covered with clay and it would have been virtually impossible to find a dry place in the mine on which to strike a match. Even today the modern match-box soon becomes damp through handling after only a short time underground. Clay pipes by their nature resist humidity and could be left down on a rock shelf or poked into a crevice in a pile of 'deads' and still remain dry enough later to enable a match to be struck. Although the miner could have easily lit his pipe from the naked flame of his lamp, the lamp itself had no self-igniting device as do the modern carbides (acetylene lamps) and would have needed a match to light it in the first place.

None of the other pipes found have such elaborate decoration but one shows the number '382' on one side and 'SCOTLAND' on the other. The stem was broken when found but probably had shown the maker's name as well. Another complete pipe has a plain bowl except for small indentations round the lip and a hole beneath the bowl for draining moisture. A short-stemmed briar pipe with Bakelite stem was also found in Salmon's Drift alongside an older clay pipe. This must have been one of the earliest briar pipes since Bakelite was only invented at the beginning of the 20th century.

It is likely that quite a lot of the older miners were pipe smokers since cigarettes were not so common in those days and indeed several pipe-smoking miners are depicted in a photograph taken at the Parkmore Mine for the Antrim Iron Ore Co. (see photograph, page 19).

Before leaving the subject of clay pipes it would be nice to think that the various motifs depicted on them could have been used by the miners as a means of identifying their own particular property since the finding of four complete pipes would suggest that their owners forgot where they had left them.

An item commonly found in the mines and something which sheds a little light on the lives of the miner is the bottle and more especially the whiskey bottle. Whether such luxuries were permitted during working hours in the mine is not known since this is not the kind of information that would be recorded in wages or cash books but it should be remembered that in those days a pint of whiskey cost 2/3d and a bottle of porter 2d. It would have been a simple matter for a miner to bring a bottle in with him and have a nip at the workface without being seen - and if the miners of the day were anything like the present generation of Irish this is understandable. Mining is thirsty work and a miner couldn't simply leave his work for a moment and go to a convenient tap for a drink of water. Water in the mines was plentiful but with the continual traffic of hutches and miners' feet and dirt spilling into drainage channels the water would have been undrinkable. He could, however, have brought a bottle of water in with him but why do this when he could have brought beer or whiskey instead. In view of the large number of spirit and beer bottles found in the mines it is highly likely that the miners took a drink now and again and visions of rollicking miners half a mile underground spring to mind.

The most common bottles found are the two-glass variety, many showing the name of the bottler or distiller e.g. J.McKenna, Ballymena, Bushmills, Murphy's or Grattan's, and quite a few unmarked, a lot of five-glass bottles were also found, mostly with no name, and a selection of P.Murphy's earthenware beer bottles. Believe it or not, some miners preferred gin. Unfortunately the labels have not withstood the years and the damp underground and rarely is one found which is completely legible. Bottles were also used as containers for sweet oil for the lamps and for tea and buttermilk. Earthenware jam jars sufficed as strong, robust tea mugs, a trifle large perhaps but more lasting than tin cups which soon rusted through.

The imprints of miners' feet in many passages is a common feature and never fails to impress and makes one wonder about the men who made them. To see for the first time the prints of hobnailed boots which have lain undisturbed for 100 and more years is an interesting experience and one can feel a close link with the miners of old so much so that it is almost possible to picture them at work. Hand imprints too are a rarer sight because they are not always easy to detect and then only in particular places. When a side road was being blocked off by deads the final airtight seal was made with wet mud which was simply plastered on by hand and pushed into cracks and corners. When the mud dried and hardened the marks of the four fingers which were the last to touch the wet surface were left clearly visible and have remained so to this clay. Their makers have long since departed.

Probably the last items to be removed from the mines were the iron rails and sleepers. The straight sections of rail could be used elsewhere and indeed it is believed that following the complete cessation of mining in Glenravel many rails were relaid in the Ballycastle coal mines where previously wooden

Above: Snibbles and (right) a miner's hutch

rails had been used. Many curved sections of rail still remain in the mines having been made for particular bends and discarded as useless when mining ceased.

It was thought that at least one miner would have left his lamp behind him when the mines were being abandoned and, indeed, one was discovered in the Essathohan Mine at Parkmore. Also, a couple of examples were located not too far away in Cargan village and it is possible that others still exist elsewhere. The lamps appear to be of two types - the one which the miner wore on his cap and which is depicted in the Parkmore Mine photograph mentioned earlier, and a larger type which could be carried in the hand probably by the mine manager and which had a large hook by which it could be hung up along the passage for general lighting. This would explain the reason for iron pegs driven into posts and walls at head height.

Both lights worked on the same principle and were known as sweet oil lamps. This was because the body of the lamp held a light oil which was soaked up by a thick wick inserted through a spout and lit just like a candle. The light from the flame would not have been much better than a candle since no provision was made for a reflector and it is likely that the flame itself gave off fumes and smoke. It is all the more remarkable, therefore, to see today the conditions under which the miners worked so successfully with such primitive equipment.

During the period of World War II mining when the bauxite mines were in operation the source of lighting was greatly improved by the use of carbide lamps. These were more robust and dependable and gave a bright, white light with a wide angle beam round head and feet. The lamp itself is in two parts. The upper part is the water container and the lower holds the carbide chips which are similar in appearance and size to road gravel. These early lamps were made of brass. The water drips through a controlled valve onto the chips below and immediately acetylene gas is given off. This is fed via a filter and tube to a fine jet located on the front of the lamp in the centre of the reflector. When the gas is lit it produces a white flame which can be adjusted in length by varying the amount of water released. Carbide lamps are still very popular today with cavers the world over and can still be easily bought. The only change in them is in the bracket for attachment to modern helmets and the fact that they are no longer made of brass. They were much used at the Arigna coal mines in Co. Leitrim.

Other items have been discovered in the Glenravel Mines but were either too big to carry out or defied identification and still remain there. It is hoped that some of the items herein mentioned will some day find their way into a local museum where they can be seen and appreciated by interested parties and preserved for all time. Without them it would be difficult to get a true picture of life and work in the mines more than a hundred years ago.

One more find which was rather unexpected and has nothing to do with mining was the discovery of a small, moisture-covered, hibernating bat in Salmon's Drift on 8th February 1975. It was clinging to the roof about 10 yards in and was not disturbed. Two weeks later a further visit was made but this time it had gone and a brief search of the roof and floor failed to locate it. This is the first and only life form found in any of the mines although there is ample evidence that foxes and badgers have used and still do use some of them as dens. The author has already had the nasty experience of being chased out of a mine by a rather large badger.

Note: Three of the original carbides used in the Templepatrick mines are in the author's possession and were occasionally used on caving trips in the early '70's. All are in perfect working order.

Chapter 13
Conclusions

Fisher's Tramway terminus
Photo courtesy of James Fisher & Sons Archives

Apart from the already-mentioned causes for the decline of the mining industry there were two main factors which would have contributed to that decline irrespective of any other reasons. These were:-

1. that there were no suitable coal reserves in Northern Ireland and therefore no smelters in Co. Antrim and the ore had to be shipped overseas.
2. the quality of the ore was not good enough for smelting on its own.

Because Nature had not completed the lateritisation process to its fullest extent the iron ore contained too much alumina and the bauxite contained too much iron. Neither ore was high enough in content to be termed a rich ore. The iron ore from Antrim had to be mixed in the smelting furnaces with other richer imported ores. The bauxite was not entirely suitable for the manufacture of aluminium and only a small quantity was used for this purpose, the remainder being processed for various products from Sulphate of Ammonia to refractory bricks. Antrim bauxite contains from 33 to 60% of alumina, not far removed from American bauxite but less than the French variety.[1] It was found that imported bauxites were much more suitable and cheaper to import so the demand for Irish bauxite declined. Not only were Irish iron ore and bauxite of inferior quality but the high cost of transport from the mines to the smelters on the mainland left little profit for the mining companies.

A little over a century ago aluminium was a virtually unknown commodity in the mineral world and it was only in 1870 that it was realised that it could be obtained from bauxite. In fact it was not until 1886 that it was produced on a practical commercial basis following the discovery of the electrolytic process of separating aluminium from bauxite. By 1900 world production was a mere 7,000 tons and the world's small bauxite output came entirely from four countries – France, USA, Italy and Co. Antrim. At that time Antrim bauxite was processed at Larne by the British Aluminium Company (founded 1895) using the 'Bayer' process.[2] This was only the first stage in the long and tedious process of converting bauxite to alumina. It was then sent to the Company's plant at Foyers on the shores of Loch Ness, Scotland, where the electrolytic reduction of metallic aluminium from alumina was carried out.

By 1940 world production had soared to 800,000 tons and by 1970 to 10 million tons. It is estimated that it takes four to six tons of raw ore to produce one ton of aluminium metal, but this depends largely on the quality of the ore being mined. Today aluminium ranks third in abundance among the Earth's minerals while iron is the fourth most common mineral.

In the years that mining flourished before World War Two about 5million tons of iron ore and a small tonnage of aluminous ore (181,932 tons from 1877-1900 and 54,651 tons during World War One) were removed by underground mining. Following the revival of the bauxite industry for the war effort, between 1941 and 1945, about 240,000 tons of this mineral were removed. Although these figures seem small in relation to the years that mining flourished it must be remembered that the ore was removed entirely by manual methods whereas mining today in this and other countries is highly automated with pneumatic cutters, mobile excavators and conveyor belts to get the ore to the surface as quickly as possible.

These figures, however, are only a small proportion of the total reserves of ore available. The miners reckoned on one ton of iron ore per cubic yard and in the Evishacrow Mine alone there were an estimated 6million tons of ore available. In the Slievenanee-Trostan tract there is reckoned to be about 7.5million tons still remaining. A similar calculation could also be made for the other areas i.e. Cargan, Carncormick, Glenariff and the plateau between there and Carnlough, and the area between Rathkenny and Broughshane.

A writer of the times (1874) noted that it would take "some hundreds of years" before the ore reserves of this area would be exhausted. A hundred and more years have now passed although that same writer was not to know that mining would be abandoned prematurely. The fact remains, however, that vast reserves of iron ore and bauxite do still exist and the question about reworking them is now one of economic feasibility with new technology, methods and uses.

Problems of a different sort may, however, arise; for example if mining was to be recommended in the Glenariff area it is probable that mining rights and licences would not be granted as it would spoil or reduce the attractiveness of one of the country's most scenic areas. The whole question of access and transport would have to be looked at again as it was a century ago, since any attempt to rework the ore deposits would require a means of getting the mined ore out of the area. Transport by road would most likely be disregarded owing to the large number of heavy trucks required, the damage these would cause to roads and the inconvenience to other road users. Rail and shipping facilities could be considered but then the problems of a century ago regarding the construction and financing of these would be resurrected. This and the fact that most of the ore reserves lie in what is now an Area of Outstanding Natural Beauty would be the chief stumbling blocks to any future exploitation of the mineral reserves, regardless of their quality.

On the other hand, there is a tendency now for each country to reinvestigate its own mineral resources to reduce the national balance of payments by reducing imports. As demand increases and techniques of processing become more sophisticated so it becomes economic to mine lower-grade deposits and to search for new sources. Recent examples of this policy have been the tests carried out for coal at Killary Glebe near Coalisland and at Ballymacilroy near Ahoghill. Back in 1979 it was thought that the bauxite deposits of Co. Antrim could be used in a new industry linked to the De Lorean car factory at Dunmurry. The bauxite is still there – the De Loreans long gone and now collectors items.

It has long been known that bauxite can be used to make non-skid road surfaces and indeed this quality has been investigated by the Department of Forensic and Industrial Science.[3] With such a complicated and disordered road network as Ireland has there would certainly be no shortage of locations for it to be laid. But this is only one of its many uses. With modern technology and the ever-increasing flow of new inventions and ideas, and new methods of using materials which we used to think of as waste, who is to say that the iron ore and bauxite reserves of Co. Antrim, which today are regarded as of poor quality, will never again become economical to work? The fact that the working of these ores in the past was abandoned does not mean that today they are no longer useful. Reworking of these deposits would greatly enhance the economy of the country and, as a side benefit, bring employment and wealth to a rural area where the jobless figures are on the increase.

Ireland is or has been one of the main base metal producers in Europe. In 1972 Ireland had the largest underground zinc mine, the largest producing lead mine, the largest producing silver mine in Europe and the world's fifteenth largest mercury mine.

Today some of the most impressive names in the mining world are searching for minerals in this country and it would seem that the Irish mining industry is sound for a long time to come. An intensive reawakening of mines and minerals is taking place throughout the mining world and deposits which years ago were discarded as waste rock are now finding new uses in the modern world. New ore beds are being discovered and and old workings being re-examined and perhaps, someday, the miners will return to Glenravel to take up where their forefathers left off.

Sources:
1. http://59.1911encyclopedia.oprg/A/AL/ALUMINIUM.htm
2. ibid.
3. Antrim Red Rocks could save lives, Ballymena Observer, 1/2/1979.

Appendices

APPENDIX 1
CLOSURE OF THE CARGAN MINE AND PROPOSAL
ON THE CONSTRUCTION OF THE DUNGONNELL TRAMWAY

Letters from:Antrim Iron Ore Company, 1st Floor, Victoria Chambers, Belfast. 23/09/1881
To: George Benn Esq., Fortwilliam Park, Belfast.

Dear Mr Benn,
We had been boring behind the dyke at Cargan for the last three months in hope of finding the ore bed but I regret to say that after boring over 200 feet we were obliged to abandon it as even if the ore exists below that depth it could not be worked. This was the last chance we had and I am now sorry to say that Cargan Mine is done and a few weeks more will remove all the ore which can be got out, so far as Cargan is concerned.

It is possible that there is ore in Dungonnell about the old fort altho our explorations in that direction were not very favourable. The Directors are however disheartened at Cargan giving up so soon and also at the heavy expenditure which would be necessary before any ore could be removed from Dungonnell and after working for ten years the shareholders are getting no return for their money. The lowest estimate we have for making the tramway round to Dungonnell is £2400, a sum which we are not prepared to spend at the present time even if we had the money.

I am sorry to say I feel disheartened myself and am afraid that with the long carriage which Irish ore has to bear there is not much chance of any money being made out of the trade. We must consider now what we intend to do and I wish to be prepared with all the information for my Directors at their first meeting. Your royalty is an important feature in the case and of course unless the Directors can see their way to find the money, viz £2400, to make the tramway so as to enable us to work Dungonnell Mine we must surrender it as there is no more ore which we can work in Cargan.

I understand you to say some time ago that you could not lend us any money or take a share in the tramway. We regret this as this is our principal difficulty. It is however possible that my Directors or some of them might see their way to find the money if they had a guarantee that a reduced royalty or fixed rent would be accepted. In any case you will see that we could not face the undertaking with the old rent hanging over us and in the event of my Directors seeing their way to go on with the tramway I would be glad if you would consider and let me know before Friday the 30th. inst. what rent you would agree to reduce to during the remainder of our lease. I think you know we are only paying Mr Hassard £50 a year for Parkmore and it is quite enough considering the trade. Crommelin Mine is still closed. Mr Crommelin has advertised it everywhere but cannot get anyone to take it. Mr Chambers has no men working. Mr Fisher has about one third of the men he had 18 months ago.

Please let me have a reply next week and oblige.

Yours faithfully,
Robert Browne, Secretary.
Belfast,
27 Sept. 1881

Dear Mr Benn,

I have your note of today. I am sorry to trouble you with business matters but I have no option as we must either give up the mines to you or continue the tramway to Dungonnell and I have already stated the difficulties are very great and until some arrangement could be arrived at with you as regards the future rent nothing can be done as regards making the rail to Dungonnell.

The miners at Cargan will be paid off as their places are worked out and I expect a number of men will be discharged during October in this way but if an arrangement could be arrived at with you it is possible these men might be put to Dungonnell either at mining or making the line of tramway. If you would authorize your solicitor Mr McLaine to attend to this matter I would go and see him. My anxiety is to keep the thing going if possible and it is with this object I wish to put before the Directors on Friday some inducement to raise the money required to make the railway and keep the mine going. I think if this was settled there would be no occasion to trouble you any more.

Yours faithfully,

Robert Browne

APPENDIX 2
SPECIAL REPORT ON THE PRIVATE RAILWAY
AND HARBOUR OF THE GLENARIFF IRON ORE COMPANY

Sirs,

The works of this railway have been thoroughly well constructed, the permanent way is in good working order, and by flattening a few of the curves it would be perfectly safe for passenger traffic. The bridges are substantial and in good order, the worst gradient is 1 in 40 nearly constant throughout. There exists an engine shed and a number of employee's houses, all well built and in good repair.

The rolling stock consists of two locomotives, a break van (sic) and 40 mineral trucks all of which are in good working order.

The pier has been substantially built of concrete up to high water level, with a superstructure of timber, and has been specially designed for the rapid shipment of iron ore by direct tipping into the vessels, being capable of exporting 200,000 tons of ore per annum. By slight alterations and further short extension of the pier a much larger export and import trade could be accommodated.

The harbour thus formed is both commodious and safe. It has a minimum depth of 25 feet of water alongside the greater part of the pier. There is an abundance of water power immediately adjacent for working hydraulic cranes etc. for the transshipment of goods.

Owing to stagnation in the iron trade these works have been practically idle for some years.

Wm. A. Traill C.E.,
Ballymena,
April 15th 1880.

(Extract from the Ballymena Observer, May 15th 1880)

Re: The Glenariff Railway and Harbour Co. Ltd.

Prospectus for the proposed completion of railway connection between the existing railways of the Glenariff Iron Ore and Harbour Co. and the Ballymena, Cushendall and Red Bay Railway Co.

Engineer's Report.

Sirs,

I have duly examined the district for the Glenariff Junction Railway and have made all necessary surveys and sections have been prepared and deposited the parliamentary plans and estimate.

The proposed line will be only 3 miles in length, and be of the 3 feet gauge, the same as on both railways which it is proposed to connect, so that through traffic can be established. The country offers no serious obstacles to the construction of such connection, the gradient throughout would be approximately constant about 1 in 40, the Red Bay railway having a constant gradient of 1 in 40, and the Ballymena and Cushendall railway gradients of 1 in 37. The proposed line is confined almost exclusively to one townland and the country traversed is all mountain land of comparative little value. Only one county road bridge and one river bridge would be required. A short tunnel, 2 furlongs in length, is necessary to avoid the residence of C. Dobbs, Esquire and to obtain the requisite working gradient. This tunnel, however, will mostly occur in the lithomarge bed, a rock comparatively easy of excavation.

Taking into consideration the cheapness of steel rails and other materials, the facility of transit to the ground, the low price of labour, the few bridges and accommodation works required and the low value of the land, I consider that the connecting link can be completed for the parliamentery estimate of £13,844, a comparatively low figure for the benefits likely to accrue therefrom.

The existing railway of the Glenariff Iron Ore Co. terminates in a zig-zag at their mines. The proposed connection would, however, join it at the lower level where there would be a station at the head of the Glenariff valley. There would be another station at the county road in Parkmore where the line joins the B.C.R.R.

Wm. A. Traill, C.E.,
Ballymena,
April 15th 1880.

(Extract from Ballymena Observer, May 15th 1880)

Special Mineral Report

Sirs,

The chief iron ore districts of the County Antrim are in the townlands of Cargan, Dungonnell, Evishacrow, Parkmore, Tuftarney, Legagrane and Skerry and southward along the valley of the Glenravel River where many iron mines have been opened and worked. These all lie immediately adjacent to the head of the proposed railway. The quantity of iron ore is practically inexhaustible. It is worked by open adits and levels from the outcrop of the ore bed and neither pumping nor winding is required.

Both here and throughout the county the quality of the ore, or per centage of metallic iron, is not such as to warrant a large expenditure on land carriage.

The Iron Ore bed also underlies the townlands of Upper Glenariff Mountains, East and West, and Cloughcorr, where it has been extensively worked along the outcrop at the head of the Glenariff valley.

The proposed connecting line, for the greater part of its length, runs immediately adjacent to the outcrop of the ore bed, and would thus afford particular facilities for removing the ore from thence, where hitherto it has been unworked.

There are also extensive deposits of aluminous ore in this district.

All the above iron ore districts lie adjacent to the proposed railway and within from 4 to 10 miles of the Harbour, so that on the average 40 miles of land carriage will be saved by this route to port. Vide Railway Map.

The White Limestone occurs in the Glenariff valley immediately adjacent to the existing railway, and for a considerable distance along side of it. The limestone is upwards of 100 feet in thickness and could be readily quarried. It is well adapted for Agricultural, Building and Chemical purposes, and would, doubtless, afford a large traffic both inland and to port for shipment.

There are several localities adjacent to Red Bay where suitable building stone - sandstone, porphyry and granite - can be obtained, which should command a large market inland, and give considerable traffic.

At Red Bay there are extensive tracts of blown sand, free from saline matter, which should develope an inland trade for building purposes etc.

Wm. A. Traill, C.E., FRGSI.,
H.M. Geological Survey of Ireland,
Ballymena, April 15th 1880.

(Extract from Ballymena Observer, May 15th 1880)

APPENDIX 3
HOUSE RENTS

CARGAN HOUSES 1883.

Felix O'Raw paid up to end of this year		6.10.0
Hugh McStay up to ending 12th June 12 fortnights		3. 0.0
Patrick McAteer		6.10.0
Alexr O'Raw		4.17.6
Catherine Fife total charged her only for 12 weeks		1.10.0
		£22. 7.6
M. Donegan	ground rent	1. 0.0
Catherine Fife	ground rent of 2 houses	2. 0.0
		£25. 7.0
	Land	5. 0.0
		£30. 0.0

(Extract from John Fisher's rent book; author's note – total above 6 pence out)

RECEIVED RENTS OF MOUNTAIN HOUSES
27th October 1886 to 29th October 1887 ending

Felix O'Raw	1 year @ 3/0 per fortnight	3.18. 0
John Hamilton	@ 2/0 per fortnight	2.12. 0
Alexr Close		2. 9. 0
John O'Raw	@ 2/6 fortnightly	3. 5. 0
Robert Gillan	@ 1/6	1.19. 0
Mick McCarthy	@ 1/6 fortnight	1.19. 0
Jas. Close	@ 1/6 do	1.19. 0
Wm McIlwaine and John Duffin		1.16. 0
		£19.17. 0

N.B. Alex Close left J. Hamilton's house time of fever and paid for Mountain house for some time only 1/6 fortnightly. John Duffin and Wm. McIlwaine not occupying house and paid none for 2 fortnights up to date. They will begin to pay for a house about 10th Decr. 1887.

(Extract from John Fisher's rent book)

MOUNTAIN HOUSE RENTS FROM 29 OCT. '87 TO 17 MARCH '88.

	wks	£. s. d
John O'Raw	29 Oct 87 to 17 Mar 88 20 @ 1/3 p.w.	1. 5. 0
James Close	29 Oct 87 to 17 Mar 88 20 @ -/9 p.w.	15. 0
Felix O'Raw	29 Oct 87 to 17 Mar 88 20 @ 1/6 p.w.	1.10. 0
Wm McIlwaine	26 Nov 87 to 3 Mar 88 14 @ -/9 p.w.	10. 6
Alex Close	29 Oct 87 to 17 Mar 88 20 @ 1/0 p.w.	1. 0. 0
Robt. Gillan	29 Oct 87 to 18 Feb 88 16 @ -/9 p.w.	12. 0
Do	18 Feb 88 to 17 Mar 88 4 @ 1/0 p.w.	4. 0
Michael McCarthy	29 Oct 87 to 17 Mar 88 20 @ -/9 p.w.	15. 0
John Hamilton	29 Oct 87 to 17 Mar 88 20 @ 1/0 p.w.	1. 0. 0

£7.11. 6

(Extract from John Fisher's rent book)

CARGAN 4 HOUSES - JOHN FISHER ESQ.
RENTS FROM 1ST JANUARY 1888 TO 17 MARCH 1888.

		£. s. d
Hugh Gillespie	11 weeks @ 2/-	1. 2. 0
Chas. O'Neill	11 " @ 2/-	1. 2. 0
Patk. McAtear	11 " @ 2/-	1. 2. 0
Alex O'Raw	11 " @ 1/6	16. 6

£4. 2. 6

(Extract from John Fisher's rent book)

APPENDIX 4
EXTRACT FROM ACCOUNTS OF THE GLENRAVEL MINE
FOR THE FORTNIGHT ENDED APRIL 17th 1869

1869   CR
APRIL 3RD   BROUGHT OVER 1148.14. 3

Ap	17	By Miners fortnightly wages				16.19. 6
	"	Aluminous ore from miners				1. 6. 0
	"	Drawer to W.McWhitty in horse drift				19. 0
	"	Men taking weights and loading carts and waggons				2. 9. 0
	"	Carting				4. 6
	"	Drivers on tramway				2. 4. 0
	"	Breaksmen Do.				1. 16. 0
	"	Platelayer & assistant				1. 5. 0
	"	Labourers for fortnight				3. 1. 2
	"	Carpenter				1. 4. 0
	"	Waggon drivers as under				
		W. Todd	8 trips			8. 0
		A. McAllister	18 Do.			18. 0
		Jas. Boyle	5 Do.			5. 0
	"	Peat for hooping wheels				1. 3
						1181.14. 8

April 17   BROUGHT OVER 1181.14. 8

		Description	cwt.	qr.	lbs.	Amount
	"	By Bran in B.Mena				7. 6
	"	" John McVey Hay				4. 5. 0
	"	Do. oats	4	0	0 @ 7/6	1. 10. 0
	"	Jas. McLaughlin oats	8	0	19 @ 7/6	3. 1. 2
	"	Messers Love & Co. for iron for new Breakwaggon				1. 4.11
	"	Blacksmiths wages including his brothers wages for helping				1. 17. 7
	"	Medicine for horses				6
	"	Coals for Smith				5. 0
	"	Boards in N.T.Crommelin				1. 2
		Nails				3. 5
						1194.10.11

(Author's note: Breaksmen = Brakesmen; Breakwaggon = Brakewaggon)

Red Bay Pier

Carters Pay Sheet From 19th March To 31st March 1888

	Tons	Cwt	of £	S	D
Patk. M Cambridge	12	9		18	8
Alex. Delargy	8	15		13	1
Michael M Killop	6	16		10	2
Henry M Auley	11	8		17	1
Mick M Caughran	2			3	
Patk. M Colloum	1	1		1	6
John Stewart	6	18		10	4
Patk. M Alister	4	8		6	7
	53	15	4	0	5

Frank Reilly

APPENDIX 5
Glenravel Mine: Tonnages of Iron Ore

The Glenravel Mine (Fisher's), 1883

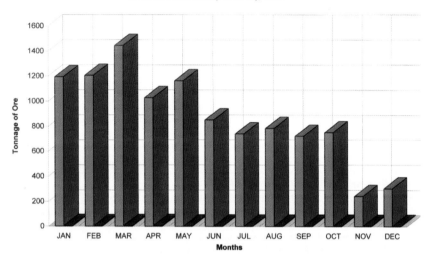

The Glenravel Mine (Fisher's Mine), 1884

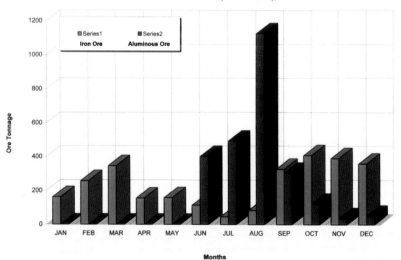

APPENDIX 6
WORKING DOWN THE MINE
(The life of a 19th Century miner)

What is surprising about being a miner is the immense horizontal distances that have to be travelled underground. Before he even gets to his work the miner may have had to creep along passages as long as from one end of Cargan to the other. In the beginning, of course, a mine level is driven near a seam of ore. But as that seam is worked out and fresh seams are followed up, the workings get further and further from the mine mouth. If it is half a mile from the entrance to the work face, that is probably an average distance; a mile or more is a possibility; there are even said to be a few mines where it is as much as three miles. But these distances bear no relation to distances above ground. For in all that mile or more as it may be, there is hardly anywhere outside the main road, and not many places even there, where a man can stand upright.

You do not notice the effect of this till you have gone a few hundred yards. You start off, stooping slightly, down the dim-lit passage, five or eight feet wide and about five high, with the walls built up with waste rock, like the stone walls in the fields. Every few yards or so there may be wooden props holding up the basalt roof; some of the props are bent and broken and alongside which you have to squeeze or duck. Usually it is bad going underfoot - mud or jagged chunks of rock, and in some mines where there is water it is as mucky as a farmyard. Also there is the track for the ore hutches, like a miniature railway track with sleepers a couple of feet apart, which is tiresome to walk on. Everything is red with the iron ore dust; there is a musty smell which seems to be the same in all mines. You press yourself against the wall to make way for lines of hutches jolting slowly towards the surface, drawn by a pit pony or pushed by a straining miner. You creep through sacking curtains and thick wooden doors which, when they are opened, let out fierce blasts of air. These doors are an important part of the ventilation system. The exhausted air is sucked out of one level, and the fresh air enters the air drift of its own accord. But if left to itself the air will take the shortest way round, leaving the deeper workings unventilated; so all the short cuts and abandoned galleries have to be partitioned off.

At the start, to walk stooping is rather a joke, but it is a joke that soon wears off. When the roof falls to four feet or less it is a tough job for anybody except a dwarf or a child. If you are a tall person you not only have to bend double, you have also got to keep your head up all the while so as to see the props and hutches and dodge them when they come. You have, therefore, a constant crick in the neck, but this is nothing to the pain in your knees and thighs. After half a mile it becomes an unbearable agony. You begin to wonder whether you will ever get to the end - still more, how on earth you are going to get back. Your pace grows slower and slower. You come to a stretch of a couple of hundred yards where it is all exceptionally low and you have to work yourself along in a squatting position. Then suddenly the roof opens out to a mysterious height – possibly the scene of an old fall of rock - and for twenty whole yards you can stand upright. The relief is overwhelming. But after this there is another low stretch of a hundred yards or a succession of dips in the roof which you have to crawl under. You go down on all fours; even this is a relief after the squatting business. But when you come to the end of the low roof and try to get up again, you find that your knees have temporarily locked and refuse to lift you. You call a halt, ignominiously, and rest for a minute or two. "Only another four hundred yards," you say to yourself encouragingly; but you feel that it might as well be another four hundred miles. But finally you do somehow creep as far as the work face. You have gone a mile and taken the best part of an hour; an experienced miner would do it in not much more than twenty minutes. Having got there, you have to sprawl in the stony red earth and get your strength back for several minutes before you can even begin to work.

Coming back is worse than going, not only because you are already tired out after a day's work but because the journey back to the mine mouth may be slightly uphill. Even the lamp you are carrying becomes a nuisance and probably when you stumble you drop it; whereupon, if it is an oil lamp, it goes out. Ducking the low roof becomes more and more of an effort, and sometimes you forget to duck. You try walking head down as the miners do, and then you bang your backbone. Even long-time miners bang their backbones fairly often. This is the reason why in some mines, where it is necessary to go about lightly clad, most of the miners have what they call "buttons down the back" - that is, a permanent scab on each vertebra. The cloth cap you wear, unlike the plastic hard hat, is little protection for the head. When your head hits the roof you feel it – more scabs. When finally you get back to the surface you have been perhaps nine hours underground and travelled two miles, and you are more exhausted than you would be by a twenty-five-mile walk above ground. For a week afterwards your thighs are so stiff that coming downstairs is quite a difficult feat; you have to work your way down in a peculiar sidelong manner, without bending the knees.

It may seem that I am exaggerating though no one who has been down an old 19th century mine and actually gone as far as the work face is likely to say so. But what I want to emphasize is this. Here is this frightful business of crawling to and fro, which to any normal person is a hard day's work in itself; and it is not part of the miner's work at all, it is merely an extra, like the city dweller's daily ride on the bus. The miner does that journey to and fro, and sandwiched in between there are seven or eight hours of savage work. When you think of the mine you think of depth, damp, darkness, dirty figures hacking at walls of stone; you don't think, necessarily, of those miles of creeping to and fro. There is the question of time, also. A miner's working shift of eight hours does not sound very long, but one has got to add on to it at least an hour a day for "travelling", more often two hours and sometimes three. Of course, the "travelling" is not technically work and the miner is not paid for it; but it is as like work as makes no difference. It is comparable, perhaps to climbing a smallish mountain before and after your day's work.

(With apologies to George Orwell)

There weren't many places where miners could stand upright

◄

Air door, Glenravel Mine

►

APPENDIX 7
IRONSTONE MINERS & RAILWAYMEN ETC
(entered in the Layd Parish register – COI – 1840 to 1920)

With the opening of the iron mines in Glenravel and Glenariff during the 2nd half of the 19th century, work became available to any glensman who fancied that type of occupation. Some of the local farmers who might otherwise have drifted out of the district for want of work, stayed at home to labour underground or on the surface. With hard cash in their pockets many, who might have remained single, married and reared sizeable families. For the more technical jobs however, experienced engineers were drawn in from outside and even from across the water. All this caused an increase in the local population.

The miners were of all religious denominations. The following details, drawn from the registers for the parish of Layd, record the names of those Church of Ireland members who worked in the mines, together with their wives and children, some of whom may still be remembered.

PARKMORE

Station Master	John McCollum, wife Susan, had Violet born 1895, John P 1897, Alfred 1898, Hugh A 1900, Robert 1902, Francis H 1903, Hellender 1905.
Engine Driver	Charles Kingston, wife Catherine, had Charles E 1875.
Boiler Maker	George Searle, m 1907 Anne Drake, aged 18 of Parkmore.
Coachman	James Nabbs, m(1) 1875 Mary Foster, had James 1876. m(2) 1881 Jane Jones of Monavert.
Mining captain	Charles H Williams, wife Elizabeth, had Charles H 1885, Grace Jane 1888, John 1890.
Timekeeper	John Dobbin.
Mining road Inspector	William J Steede, wife Sarah, had Hannah 1887.
Miners	Adam Maqillon, wife Nancy, had Joseph 1873. Samuel Steede, m 1876 Ellen Millar of Parkmore, had Margaret 1877. William Moore, m 1875 Eliza Weir of Parkmore, had Catherine 1877, Jane Mary 1879, Ellen 1881, Lizzie 1883, Robert J 1886, Jane 1891. Thomas Stars, wife Rebecca, had John 1878. James Millar, m 1876 Arsminta McIntosh of Parkmore, had Ellen 1879. Hugh Young, wife Sarah, had William John 1880. John Ross, wife Martha, had James 1881.

William J Steed, wife Sarah, had Sarah 1883.
Robert Steed, wife Margaret, had Elizabeth 1887.
John McCleery, wife Lizzie, had Lizzie 1883.
Henry Freeburn, wife n/k, had Samuel 1897.
Samuel Freeburn of Parkmore, m 1922 Ellen Moore of Parkmore.
David McDowell.
Samuel McSweeney, wife Martha, had William 1892, Margaret & Elizabeth 1894, Anne 1897
Samuel McSweenet, wife Fanny, had Martha 1906.
Robert McSweeney.
James Dobbin, son of John (timekeeper), m 1912 Sarah McSweeney of Parkmore.
Thomas McSweeney.
William McCluig, wife Lydia, had Martha 1893.
Thomas McCluig, wife Ellen, had Thomas 1895.
Joseph McCluig, son of William, m 1899 Margaret Hilditch of Carrickfergus.
Samuel Ramsey, son of John, captain miner, m 1895 Mary Steed, 16½, dtr of John, miner.
James Anderson, son of William, miner, m 1899 Martha of Parkmore, dtr of Gillin, J, miner, had Jamie 1901.

Labourer	Robert Anderson, wife Ellen, had Mary Katherine 1899.

RETREAT

Station Master	Samuel McKinley, wife Catherine, had Margaret 1882, Mary 1883, John Turnly, 1885.
Milesman	William Hamilton, wife Nancy.

GLENARIFF PIER

Manager	John Dixon, wife Sarah, had Athol Osman St John 1878, Ivy Ethelreda 1879, Adina Sarah 1881, Hilda Mabel 1882, Harold Ivan 1884.
Engine Driver	William Kithey, wife Emma, had George 1876, John 1878, Sarah Anne 1882, Jane 1884.
Pile Driver	Robert S Reynolds, m 1875 Margaret Bray of Waterfoot.
Miner	Stewart Martin, wife Margaret, had James 1878, Stewart 1882.

TROSTAN

Miner	John Norton, wife Nancy, had Catherine 1875.

CARGAN

Engine Driver	Matthew McQuitty, son of William mine manager, m 1911 Hannah Steed, dtr of William miner, had George 1922.

CUSHENDALL

Banker Manager	James Parke Cinnamond of Glenburn, Cushendall, wife Isabella, had Annie Long 1885, James Parke 1886, George McKerrow 1888, Katherine McDonnell 1889, Olive 1891, Lisle Parke 1894, Ellen Marguerite 1895, Hubert Parke 1897, Robert Stewart 1902.

APPENDIX 8
Names and occupations associated with Fisher's mines

AGNEW, HENRY	SUPPLIER OF OATS
AGNEW, OWEN	WAGGON DRIVER
BARRENS, H	SUPPLIER OF OATS
BOYLE, JAMES	WAGGON DRIVER
BRADSHAW, HUGH	SUPPLIER OF OATS
CAMPBELL, PAT	SUPPLIER OF OATS
CAREY, HUGH	SUPPLIER OF OATS
CAREY, PAT	SUPPLIER OF OATS
CRAIG, MR	HARNESS REPAIRER, SADDLER
CURRY, HUGH	SUPPLIER OF OATS (CLOUGH)
CURRY, JOHN	SUPPLIER OF OATS
CUSHENAN, A	BLACKSMITH
CUSHENAN, JOHN	BLACKSMITH
CUSHENAN, THOMAS	BLACKSMITH'S HELPER
DELARGY, BERNARD	UNKNOWN (GLENARIFF)
DORNAN, R	SUPPLIER OF OATS
DORNAN, W	SUPPLIER OF OATS
DOUGHERTY, JOHN	SUPPLIER OF HAY
GRAHAM, WILLIAM	SUPPLIER OF PEATS
IRELAND, H	CARTER
KENNEDY, W	HARDWARE SUPPLIER (N/CROMMELIN)
LOUGHRIDGE, DAN	SUPPLIER OF HAY
LOVE, MR	IRONMONGER?
MADDEN, PATRICK	SUPPLIER OF OATS
MADILL, W	SUPPLIER OF HAY
MCALISTER, DANIEL	SUPPLIER OF WAGGON BOARDS (C/DALL)
MCALISTER, E	SUPPLIER OF OATS
MCALISTER, W	WAGGON DRIVER
MCALLISTER, ALEXANDER	WAGGON DRIVER
MCBURNEY, JOHN	SUPPLIER OF OATS
MCCANN, D	STONE BREAKER
MCCANN, JAMES	CARTER

MCCAUGHAN, HUGH	SUPPLIER OF LIME
MCCREADY, JAMES	RED BAY DRIVER
MCGAUGHAN, JERRY	SUPPLIER OF WOOD PRODUCTS?
MCGAUGHEN, JOHN	WEIGHING OATS
MCILWAINE, DAVID	SUPPLIER OF OATS
MCKEESICK, F	COAL SUPPLIER? (AT RED BAY)
MCKEEVER, JAMES	CARPENTER
MCKEON, JOHN	SUPPLIER OF OATS
MCKEON, PATRICK (DEC'D)	SUPPLIER OF HAY
MCKEON, RANDLE	EXECUTOR OF PATRICK MCKEON
MCKEOWN, MICHAEL	SUPPLIER OF HAY
MCLAUGHLIN, CHARLES	SUPPLIER OF OATS
MCLAUGHLIN, JAMES	SUPPLIER OF OATS
MCLAUGHLIN, JOHN	SUPPLIER OF HAY
MCMULLAN, MISS S	SUPPLIER OF OATS
MCVEY, JOHN	SUPPLIER OF HAY
MCWHITTY, WILLIAM	MINER
MULLAN, CHARLES	SUPPLIER OF OATS
O'BOYLE, JAMES	WAGGON DRIVER
O'LOAN, PATRICK	SUPPLIER OF OATS
O'NEILL, G	SUPPLIER OF OATS
O'NEILL, JOHN	SUPPLIER OF HAY
O'RAW, HUGH	MINE CAPTAIN
O'RAW, JOHN	SUPPLIER OF OATS (N/CROMMELIN)
O'RAW, W	SUPPLIER OF OATS
REILLY, PETER	SUPPLIER OF LIME
ROSS, W	SUPPLIER OF OATS
TODD, WILLIAM	WAGGON DRIVER

MINERS ETC	1886
BRETT, (BIRT), BERNARD	MINER
BRETT, (BIRT), DENIS	MINER
BRETT, (BIRT), HENRY	MINER

BRETT, (BIRT), THOMAS	MINER
CAMERON, ROBERT	MINER
CLOSE, ALEXANDER	MINER
CLOSE, JAMES	MINER
COULTER, JOHN	MINER
DONEGAN, FRANCIS	MINER
DORNAN, HARRISON	MINER
DUFFIN, JOHN	MINER
DUFFIN, RODGER	MINER
GILLAN, ROBERT	MINER
GILLESPIE, HUGH	MINER
GREEN, WILLIAM	MINER
HAMILTON, JOHN	MINER
KENNEDY, ANDY	MINER
KERR, THOMAS A	MINER
MAGILL, CHARLES	MINER
MARCHELL, ALEXANDER	MINER
MCATEER, DANIEL	MINER
MCATEER, JOHN	MINER
MCATEER, PATRICK	MINER
MCCAMBRIDGE, MICHAEL	MINER
MCCARTHY, MICHAEL	MINER
MCCORMICK, CHARLES	MINER
MCCRORY, ROBERT H	MINER
MCGONNELL, DANIEL	MINER
MCILWAINE, WILLIAM	MINER
MCKEOWN, JAMES	MINER
MCMULLAN, CHARLES	MINER
MCWHITTY, ROBERT JAMES	MINER
MCWHITTY, WILLIAM	MINER
MOONEY, HUGH	MINER
MURDOCK, ROBERT	MINER
O'LOAN, PATRICK	MINER
O'NEILL, CHARLES (LONG)	MINER
O'NEILL, JOHN	MINER
O'RAW, ALEXANDER	MINER
O'RAW, FELIX	MINER
O'RAW, PATRICK	MINER
REYNOLDS, THOMAS	MINER
SAVAGE, JOHN	MINER
SAVAGE, WILSON	MINER
SCULLION, ROBERT	HELPER AT TRAMEND
SHANNON, NEIL	MINER
WALSH, JAMES	MINER
WRIGHT, WILLIAM	CARPENTER

APPENDIX 9
Sample of mine site inventory

MINE SITE INVENTORY

SITE NO.	O.F. Report	109
NAME	Salmon's Drift	
ALT NAME	Solomon's Drift	

MINING DISTRICT	TOWNLAND	COUNTY
GLENRAVEL	Skerry East	ANTRIM

SHEETS		
6" to 1Mile	1:25000	1:50000
Sheet 24	Activity Map Glens of Antrim	Sheet 9 Ballymena

Grid Reference			
15327 19856	Source MAP ☑	GPS ☑	Image file ☑

MAIN MINERALS	OTHER RECORDS
Iron ore, bauxite	DED plans - M3/619; Author's slides, VHS, BBC film (1975), author's log book, Walter Cameron's video, Descent Magazine

FEATURE NO.	TYPE	FUNCTION	CONDITION	THREATS
1	MINE	ADIT	OPEN	Dumping & collapse
2				
3				
4				
5				
6				

CONSERVATION ISSUES	COMMENTS
Entrance now gated but needs possible excavation at adit mouth to prevent water running in. Bats seen in this mine therefore needs protecting.	Extensive workings, mostly comfortable to walk in. Mucky pool inside adit mouth then dry. Used for countless field trips since early 1970's - BBC, Belfast Geologists Society, rambling groups, educational trips, EHS, H&S etc. Worked by Crommelin Mining Co Ltd 1891 - 31/12/1923.

SITE OWNER	
Paddy McQuillan, Tuftarney	

AUTHOR	DATE	REVISED BY	DATE
K O'Hagan	05/05/2011	K O'Hagan	10/08/2016

APPENDIX 10
Wages records Glenravel mine 1868-69

	£	s	d			£	s	d
				Oct-19 Alexr McAlister 3 trips & 10½ days work		1	0	6
Oct-05 Miners wages	43	14	3	(contd) bank for cashing			3	9
carting from streams etc	0	10	6	iron, steel, nails Mr Love			16	5
drivers, breaksmen	2	4	0	Total	213	5	9½
men taking weights	2	5	0					
plate layers	2	10	0	Brought over		213	5	9½
labourers	3	0	3	Miners wages		43	18	10
carpenters, sawyers	3	7	0	Oct-31 men taking weights		2	10	0
blacksmith	1	0	0	carting from streams		0	15	0
oats John Breet	1	10	6	drivers for tramway horses		2	0	0
Owen Agnew driving waggons 24 trips	1	4	0	breaksmen		1	12	0
Jas O'Boyle driving waggons & pier work	1	3	2	plate layers		2	15	0
same Alexr McAlister	1	0	0	labourers		0	14	11½
glazed cloth for men's shoulders in drifts	0	3	0	carpenters, sawyers		1	3	0
bank for cashing		2	1	blacksmith		0	18	0
Oct-19 Miners wages	47	16	6	Redbay waggon drivers (as under)				
carting from streams etc	1	18	6	Owen Agnew		1	0	0
men taking weights	2	15	0	Jas O'Boyle		1	0	0
drivers, breaksmen	2	18	0	A McAlister		1	0	0
plate layers	2	10	0	bran		0	7	6
labourers	1	13	5½	oats H O'Raw		1	11	3
carpenters, sawyers	2	3	6	oats Gregory O'Neill		1	18	0
carting ore to Red Bay month end	80	13	2	grease, oil, from 24th Aug to date		2	1	0
oats	1	11	9	hay for horses, small part to Red Bay		4	0	0
blacksmith	1	4	0	hay delivered at Red Bay		1	8	0
Owen Agnew driving waggons 24 trips	1	4	0	Total	283	18	4
Jas O'Boyle 21 trips 1 & half days	1	3	6					

APPENDIX 11
GLOSSARY OF MINING TERMS

Adit – horizontal entrance to mine to provide access or for drainage purposes.
Air door – doorway within the mine which could be blocked off to divert air for ventilation.
Air drift – horizontal or inclined passage driven for ventilation purposes.
Air shaft – vertical shaft for ventilation purposes.
Aluminous ore – ore of Aluminium i.e. Bauxite.
Brushings – band of clayey rock between the ore seam and the roof; only a few inches thick.
Captain – the mine manager.
Deads – waste rock containing no ore used to block off side workings or to support the roof.
Dollies – short, stout timbers used in low workings to support roof.
Drift – horizontal mine level (from the verb `to drive')
Driving – the act of cutting or making a level into or within the mine.
Dyke – volcanic intrusion of very hard rock which had the effect of displacing the ore seam.
Fathom – six feet; the measure by which the mine was progressed.

Gaten (gatten, gauton) – drainage channel in mine passage (in photo it is channel on right) ➤
Horse road – passage suitable for use by horses for hauling hutches out of the mine.
Hutch – small four-wheeled bogies set on rails for removal of ore out of mine.
Jumper – long heavy iron rock drill, chisel-pointed and hand-operated.
Level – mine passage for access to workings.
Main road – main thoroughfare into, within and out of the mine.
Outcrop – ore seam exposed at the surface.
Pavement – local term for decomposing ferruginous bauxite, usually the floor of the excavated galleries etc.
Pisolithic – used to describe iron ore containing pea-sized nodules of iron.
Pot-ass – bulge protruding downwards from the roof requiring shoring.
Rickety – ratchet-operated rock drill.
Room and pillar – method of mining where columns of rock are left standing to support roof.
Side road – level off main road to working places.
Snibble – iron bar to jam hutch wheels for braking purposes.
Sweet oil – similar to light engineering oil, for miners lamps.
Sylvester – chain and ratchet device for removing timbers on abandonment of mine.
Tramend – terminus of mineral tramway.
Tramway – miner's term for Fisher's horse-drawn railway.
Trees and lids – props and wedges for roof support; mine timbers.
Water course – drainage channel within mine (same as gaten).

APPENDIX 12
JOHN FISHER BIOGRAPHY

The *Barrow Herald* of last Saturday's issue published a supplement giving an excellent portrait of the above gentleman, with the following biographical sketch, under the heading of 'Mr. John Fisher, Mayor of Barrow':

Mr. John Fisher, who resides at Fairfield, Newbarns, and has been a councillor for that ward for the last twelve years, and who was elected the Mayor of Barrow for the current year, was born in one of the farmhouses in the village of Barrow, and is forty-four years of age. He is the second son of the late Mr James Fisher, whose family is one of the oldest in the district, and who, in addition to his shipping business, farmed a considerable part of the land on which Barrow now stands. The present Mayor received the early part of his education in the Newbarns School (which then stood in the Abbey Road, and was the only school in the district), and later in private schools in the town, and at St. Bees, from whence he entered his father's office. After being at business a short time he was sent to Ireland to manage his father's estate and his Glenravel Iron Ore Mines. Returning to Barrow about three years later, he was admitted a partner - along with his older brother – in their father's business, which then assumed the name of James Fisher & Sons. On the death of their father, in 1873, the partner-ship was dissolved, Mr. John Fisher returning to Ireland to take over that branch of the business, together with a number of vessels, and subsequently he built other ships for himself. At the age of twenty-eight he bought up the whole of the interest of the Barrow business, and again returned to Barrow, subsequently taking into partnership his younger brother, the joint business being now conducted from the Barrow office.

The firm, in addition to its ship-owning, has a large merchant's business, and they are also Lloyds' agents, and American Lloyds' agents, agents for the Liverpool and Glasgow Under-writers' Associations, honorary agents for the Shipwrecked Mariners' Society, Vice-Consuls for Portugal and Mexico, and agents for numerous other societies and companies. About fifty years ago the late Mr. James Fisher was appointed shipping agent by Messrs. Schneider, Hannay & Co., and subsequently to the Barrow Hematite Steel Co., and this connection has continued without intermission down to the present day. At one time the fleet of vessels managed by Messrs. Fisher numbered about eighty sail, but owing to the altered requirements of later times this number has decreased, it having become necessary to employ steamships to meet the wants of more rapid transit. The firm is known all over the World, and

its present fleet of steam and sailing vessels, numbering forty-six, is the largest of its kind in the United Kingdom.

The Glenravel iron ore mines, which were opened about thirty years ago by the late Mr. James Fisher, were brought to his notice by the late Rev Father McCauley, parish priest of Glenravel and the Braid, who up to the time of his death was a warm friend of the family, and the whole of the mine owners liberally subscribed towards the erection in Glenravel of a monument to his memory. These mines were the first of the description ever worked in Ireland. Subsequently, other similar mines were opened, and what was once a purely agricultural district became a busy place, large sums of money being weekly paid in wages. To cope with the ore traffic a railway of about 17 miles long was constructed, and by this route the beautiful glens of Antrim, now so well known and so much frequented by the tourist, are reached. We believe this was the first narrow gauge railway constructed in Ireland. Two other railways on the same principle were soon afterwards made in the district, and more recently numerous other narrow gauge railways have been made in different parts of Ireland.

In order to provide suitable accommodation for the miners Mr. John Fisher built a number of houses, and other gentlemen added more, until what he commenced grew into a village, with school accommodation for about 400 children. The village is on the main road between Ballymena and Cushendall and is named Fisherstown, as a standing memorial of the Fisher family, who are known as well in

Mid-Antrim as at Barrow. We might also mention that a project is on foot to erect a large manufactory in Glenravel for the production of products derived from bauxite, of which there are large deposits in the district, and if this is carried out it is likely to further increase the village.

About 30 years ago the late Mr James Fisher bought the Claggan estate, which is situated at the head of the Braid Valley, the residence having been built for a shooting lodge by one of the Lords O'Neill, and it is here Mr. Fisher spends his leisure time, and he is never happier than when out on the moors or fishing in the streams which run through the place. The Mayor, being a bachelor, will have the assistance of his sister, Mrs Bradshaw, as Mayoress, and that lady will discharge the duties of the office during the ensuing year.

(From Ballymena Weekly Telegraph, 24/11/1894)